easy Guitar Top Pops

787.61 EAS

Wise Publications
London/New York/Paris/Sydney/Copenhagen/Madrid

Exclusive Distributors:
Music Sales Limited
8-9 Frith Street,
London W1V 5TZ, England.
Music Sales Pty Limited
120 Rothschild Avenue,
Rosebery, NSW 2018,
Australia.

Order No. AM951962
ISBN 0-7119-7281-8
This book © Copyright 1999 by Wise Publications

Compiled by Peter Evans
Music arranged by Rob Smith
Music processed by Andrew Shiels
Cover design by Studio Twenty, London
Cover photography by Julian Hawkins
Printed in the United Kingdom by
The Bath Press, Bath

Your Guarantee of Quality
As publishers, we strive to produce every book to the
highest commercial standards.
The music has been freshly engraved and the book
has been carefully designed to minimise awkward
page turns and to make playing from it a real
pleasure.
Particular care has been given to specifying acid-
free, neutral-sized paper made from pulps which
have not been elemental chlorine bleached. This
pulp is from farmed sustainable forests and was
produced with special regard for the environment.
Throughout, the printing and binding have been
planned to ensure a sturdy, attractive publication
which should give years of enjoyment.
If your copy fails to meet our high standards,
please inform us and we will gladly replace it.

Music Sales' complete catalogue describes
thousands of titles and is available in full colour
sections by subject, direct from Music Sales Limited.
Please state your areas of interest and send a
cheque/postal order for £1.50 for postage to:
Music Sales Limited, Newmarket Road,
Bury St. Edmunds, Suffolk IP33 3YB.

Other titles in the
Easy Guitar series...
Classic Hits
Order No. AM951940

Chart Toppers
Order No. AM951930

All-Time Hits
Order No. AM951951

Addicted To Love

Words & Music by Robert Palmer

1. The lights are on but you're not home, your mind___ is not your
(Verse 2 see block lyric)

own. Your heart sweats, your bo - dy shakes, an - oth - er kiss is what it

takes. You can't sleep, (no) you can't eat, there's no doubt___ you're in
(Verse 3(%) see block lyric)

deep.___ Your throat is tight, you can't breathe,___ an - oth - er kiss is all you

need. Oh___ you___ like to think that you're im - mune___ to the stuff, oh yeah.___

It's clo - ser to the truth to say you   can't get en - ough, you know you're

1.

gon - na have to face__ it, you're ad - dic - ted   to   love.__ 2. You   see   the

2.%

-dic - ted   to   love.__   You might__ as well   face it, you're ad - dic - ted   to   love.__   You might__

as well   face it, you're ad - dic - ted   to   love._____ You   might__ as well   face it, your're ad -

D. % *to fade*

- dic - ted   to   love.__   You   might__ as well   face it, you're ad - dic - ted   to   love.__ 3. The lights are

Verse 2:   You see the signs but you can't read
You're running at a different speed
Your heart beats in double time
Another kiss and you'll be mine
A one-track mind, you can't be saved
Oblivion is all you crave
If there's some left for you
You don't mind if you do.

Verse 3(%):   The lights are on but you're not home
Your will is not your own
Your heart sweats, your teeth grind
Another kiss and you'll be mine.

Albatross

Composed by Peter A. Green

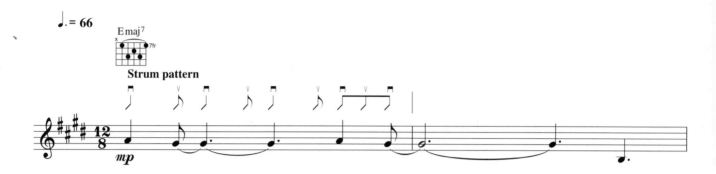

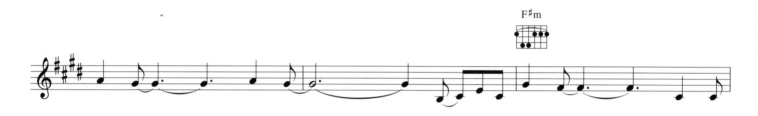

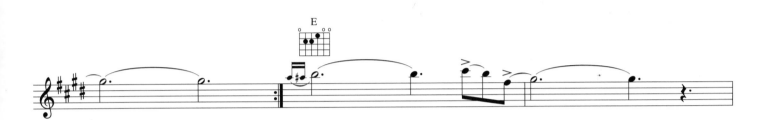

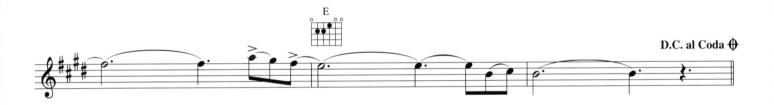

⊕ Coda

7

All Shook Up

Words & Music by Otis Blackwell & Elvis Presley

A - well - a, bless my soul, what's wrong with me? I'm

itch - ing like a man on a fuz - zy tree. My friends say I'm act - in'

queer as a bug I'm in love I'm all shook up! Mm

mm oh, oh, yeah, yeah! My

hands are shak - y and my knees are weak, I can't seem to stand on my

own two feet,____ Who do you thank when you have such luck?__ I'm in

E♭7 F7

love! I'm all shook up!__ Mm__ mm, oh, oh, yeah,__

B♭ E♭7 B♭ E♭7

yeah!_____ Please don't ask me what's a
                                    2. tongue gets tied when I

on my mind,__ I'm a lit-tle mixed up but I'm feel-in' fine.__ When I'm
try to speak,__ my in - side shakes like a leaf on a tree. There's

E♭7 F7

near that girl that I love best,__ my heart beats so it scares
on-ly one cure for this soul of mine,__ that's to have the girl that I

__ me to death! She touched my hand, what a chill I got,__ her
love so fine!

kis - ses are like___ a vol - ca - no that's hot!___ I'm proud to say she's my

but - ter cup,___ I'm in love! I'm all shook up!___ Mm___

1.

mm oh, oh, yeah,___ yeah!_____ 2. My

2.

yeah! I'm all shook up!___ Mm___ mm oh,

oh, yeah,___ yeah! I'm all shook up!___ Mm___ mm oh,

oh, yeah,___ yeah! I'm all shook up!___

All That She Wants

Words & Music by Buddha & Joker

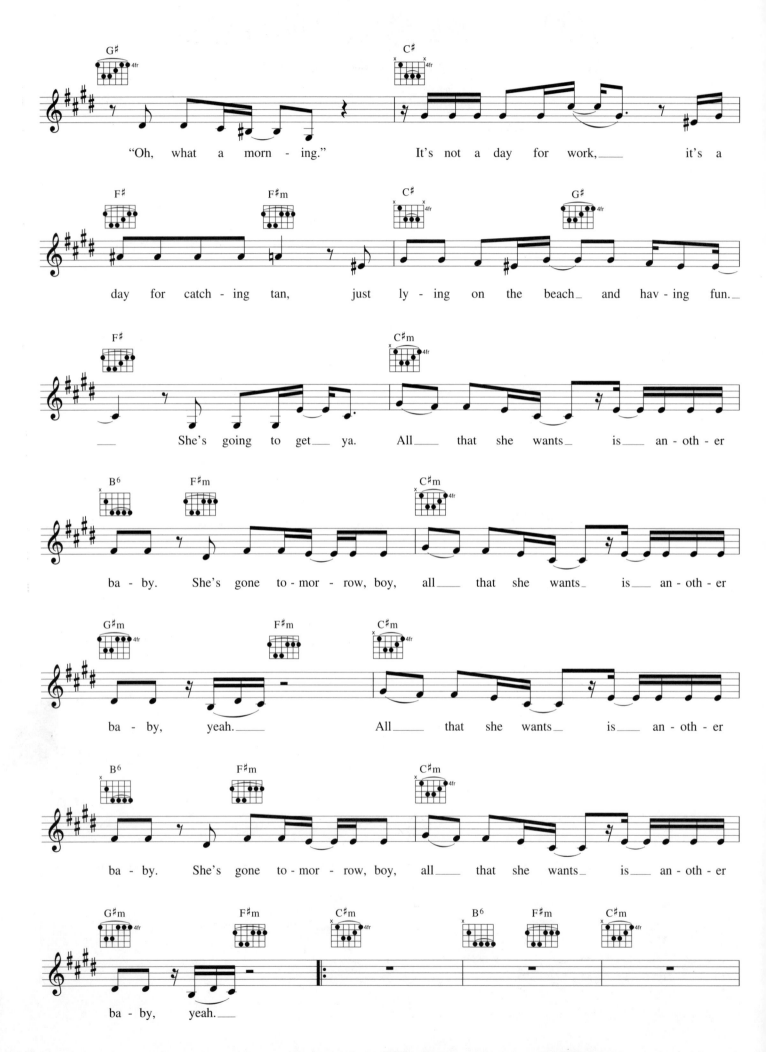

American Pie

Words & Music by Don McLean

A long, long time a-go I can still re-mem-ber how that

mu-sic used to make me smile. And I knew if I had my chance that

I could make those peo-ple dance and may-be they'd be hap-py for a while.

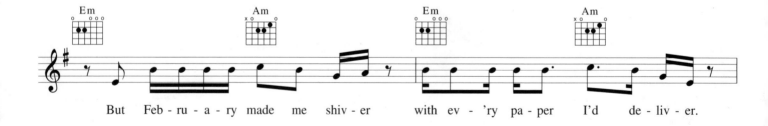

But Feb-ru-a-ry made me shiv-er with ev-'ry pa-per I'd de-liv-er.

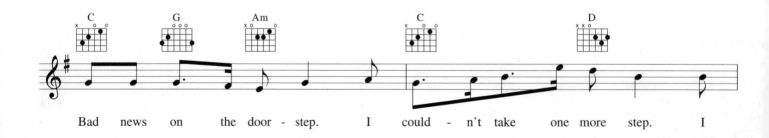

Bad news on the door-step. I could-n't take one more step. I

can't re-mem-ber if I cried when I read a-bout his wid-owed bride.

Some-thing touched me deep in-side the day the mu-sic died. So

Chorus ♩= 112

Strum pattern

bye - bye Miss A-mer-i-can Pie, drove my Chev-y to the lev-ee but the

lev - ee was dry. Them good ole boys were drink-in'

To Coda ⊕

whis-key and rye, sing-in' "This-'ll be the day that I die,

this-'ll be the day that I die,"

15

Verse

1. Did you___ write the book of love___ and do you___ have faith in
(Verses 2–4 see block lyric)

God a - bove?___ If the bi - ble tells___ you so___ Now do

you___ be - lieve___ in rock and roll.___ Can mu - sic save your

mor - tal soul___ and can you teach me how to dance___

real slow?_____ Well, I know that you're_ in

love with him___ 'cause I_____ saw you danc - in' in the gym.___ You

16

both kicked off___ your shoes.___ Man, I dig those rhy - thm and

blues.___ I was a lone - ly teen - age___ bronc - in' buck___ with a

pink car - na - tion and a pick - up truck.__ But I knew I___ was out___

___ of luck___ the day___ the mu - sic died.__

1.2.3.   I start - ed sing - ing:

4. He was sing - in' bye - bye, Miss A -

- mer - i - can Pie.__ Drove my Chev - y to the lev - ee but the lev - ee was dry.__ Them

17

good ole boys__ were drink - in' whis - key and rye,___ sing - in' "This 'll be the day__ that I___

die, this 'll be the day__ that I___ die."_____

Freely

Strum pattern

I met a girl who sang__ the blues___ and I asked her for some hap - py news.___ But

she just smiled and turned a - way._____ I went down to the sa - cred store__ where I

heard the mu - sic years be - fore. But the man there said the mu - sic would - n't

play._____ And in the streets the child - ren screamed,__ the

lov - ers cried__ and the po - ets dreamed,__ but not a word was spo - ken, the

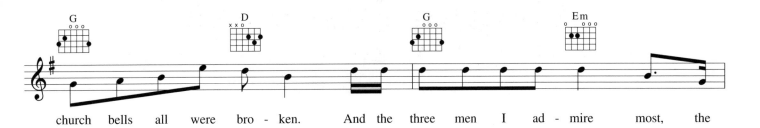

church bells all were bro - ken. And the three men I ad - mire most, the

Fa - ther, Son and the Ho - ly Ghost. They caught the last train for the coast the day the mu - sic

D. 𝄋 al Coda ⊕   Coda ⊕

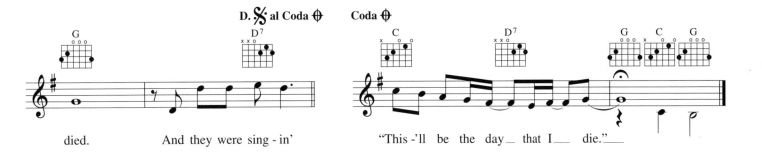

died.   And they were sing - in'   "This -'ll be the day ___ that I ___ die." ___

Verse 2:   Now for ten years we've been on our own, and moss grows fat on a rollin' stone
                But that's not how it used to be when the jester sang for the king and queen
                In a coat he borrowed from James Dean and a voice that came from you and me
                Oh and while the king was looking down, the jester stole his thorny crown
                The courtroom was adjourned, no verdict was returned
                And while Lenin read a book on Marx the quartet practised in the park
                And we sang dirges in the dark
                The day the music died.
                We were sing in' . . . bye-bye . . . *etc.*

Verse 3:   Helter-skelter in the summer swelter the birds flew off with a fallout shelter
                Eight miles high and fallin' fast, it landed foul on the grass
                The players tried for a forward pass, with the jester on the sidelines in a cast
                Now the half-time air was sweet perfume while the sergeants played a marching tune
                We all got up to dance but we never got the chance
                'Cause the players tried to take the field, the marching band refused to yield
                Do you recall what was revealed
                The day the music died.
                We were sing in' . . . bye-bye . . . *etc.*

Verse 4:   And there we were all in one place, a generation lost in space
                With no time left to start again
                So come on, Jack be nimble, Jack be quick, Jack Flash sat on a candlestick
                'Cause fire is the devil's only friend
                And as I watched him on the stage my hands were clenched in fists of rage
                No angel born in hell could break that Satan's spell
                And as the flames climbed high into the night to light the sacrificial rite
                I saw Satan laughing with delight the day the music died.
                He was singin' . . . bye-bye . . . *etc.*

Behind The Mask

Words & Music by Ryuichi Sakomoto, Chris Mosdell & Michael Jackson

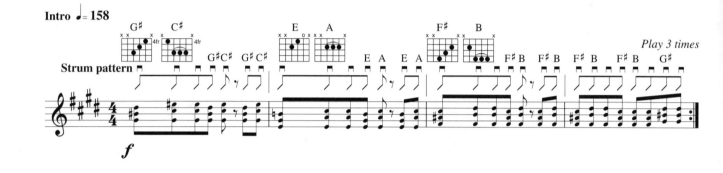

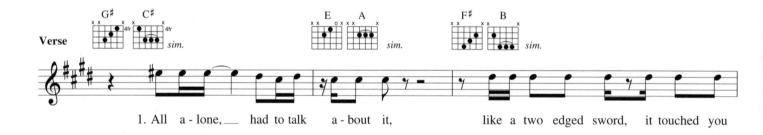

1. All a - lone,___ had to talk a - bout it, like a two edged sword, it touched you

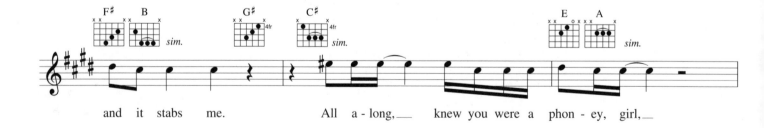

and it stabs me. All a - long,___ knew you were a phon - ey, girl,___

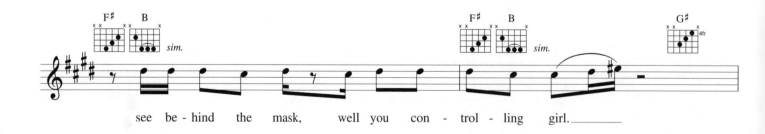

see be - hind the mask, well you con - trol - ling girl._____

Verse 4(%):   I walked around suffering in my doom
When I come to you, you're sitting in your room
The truth in you, I have longed to trace
To take off the mask so I can see your face.

Bridge Over Troubled Water

Words & Music by Paul Simon

* Original recording sounds in E♭

1. When you're

wea - ry, / feel - in' small; / when tears are
down and out, / when you're on the street, / when eve - ning

in / your eyes, / I'll dry them all. ____
falls, / so hard, / I will com - fort you. ____

I'm on your side, / oh, when times __ get rough
I'll take your part, / oh, when dark - ness comes

and friends just can't   be   found. ⎫ Like a bridge o - ver
and pain is all   a - round. ⎬

trou - bled wa - ter,   I will lay me down. Like a bridge o - ver

trou - bled wa - ter,   I will lay me down.

1.

2. When you're

2.

down.

3. Sail on sil - ver girl,   sail on by.

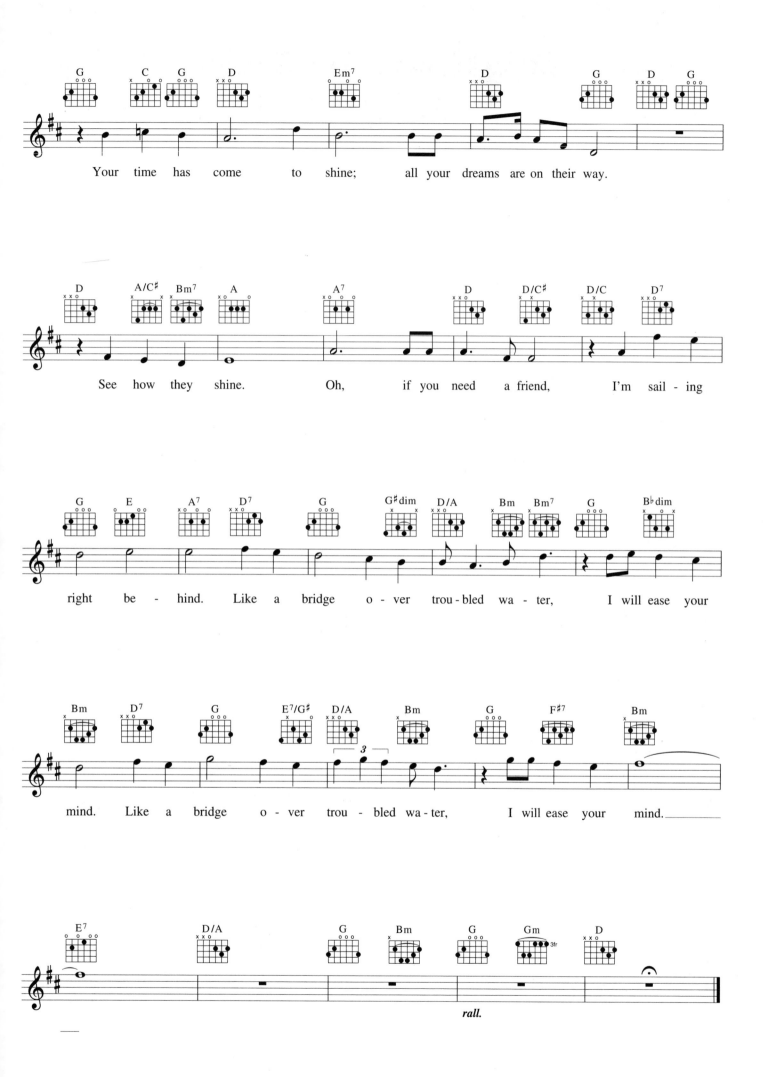

Brothers In Arms

Words & Music by Mark Knopfler

burn to__ be bro - thers__ in arms.__

2. Through these fields of de -

Verse

- struc - tion,__ bap - ti - sms of fire.__

(Verse 3(%) see block lyric)

I've wit - nessesd your suf - fering as the bat - tle raged

high - er. And though they did hurt me so bad__

in the fear and__ a - larm,__ you__ did not__ de -

To Coda ⊕

(Instrumental)

- sert me my bro - thers__ in arms.__

27

There's so ma-ny dif-ferent

worlds, so ma-ny dif-ferent suns, and we have just one

world, but we live in dif-ferent ones.

(Instrumental)

D. %: al Coda ⊕

3. Now the sun's gone to hell

⊕ Coda

Repeat to fade

(Instrumental)

Verse 3(%):   Now the sun's gone to hell and the moon's riding high
Let me bid you farewell, every man has to die
But it's written in the starlight and every line of your palm
We're fools to make war on our brothers in arms.

28

Country House

Words & Music by Damon Albarn, Graham Coxon, Alex James & David Rowntree

I'm a pro - fess - 'nal cy - nic, but my heart's not in it; I'm

pay - ing the price_ of liv - ing life at the li - mit, caught_ up in the

To Coda

cent - 'ry's_ anx - i - e - ty." Yes, it preys on him,_

_ he's get - ting thin._ Now he

Chorus

lives in a house, a ve - ry big house in the coun - try,

watch - ing af - ter - noon re - peats and the food he eats_ in the coun -

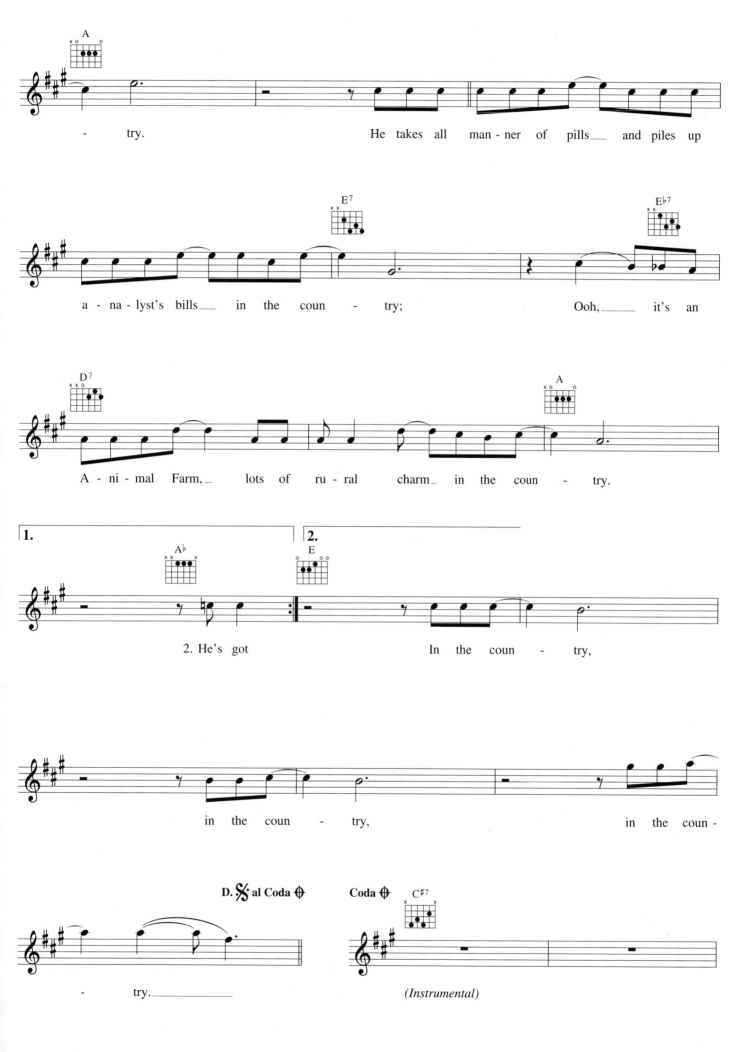

-try.   He takes all man-ner of pills___ and piles up

a-na-lyst's bills___ in the coun-try;   Ooh,___ it's an

A-ni-mal Farm,___ lots of ru-ral charm___ in the coun-try.

1.   2. He's got   In the coun-try,

in the coun-try,   in the coun-

D. S. al Coda ⊕   Coda ⊕

-try.___   (Instrumental)

Middle 8

A — E — Blow, blow me out, I am —

— so sad, I don't know why. —

1. — 2. Oh, he

Chorus

A — E⁷ — lives in a house, a ve-ry big house in the coun-try,
(Chorus 2 see block lyric)

E♭⁷ — D⁷ — watch-ing af-ter-noon re-peats and the food he eats in the coun-

A — -try. He takes all man-ner of pills and piles up

32

a - na - lyst's bills__ in the coun - try; Ooh,____ it's like an

1.
A - ni - mal Farm,__ lots of ru - ral charm__ in the coun - try.

2.
Oh,_____ he - try._____ Ooh, la la

(la.)

Repeat to fade

Verse 2:   He's got morning glory
              And life's a different story
              Everything's going 'Jackanory'
              In touch with his own mortality
              He's reading Balzac, knocking back Prozac
              It's a helping hand that makes you feel wonderfully bland
              Oh, it's the century's remedy
              For the faint at heart, a new start

Chorus 2:   He lives in a house, a very big house in the country
              He's got a fog in his chest
              So he needs a lot of rest in the country
              He doesn't drink, smoke, laugh
              Takes herbal baths in the country
              But you'll come to no harm
              On the Animal Farm in the country.

Verse 3:   *Instrumental*

California Dreaming

Words & Music by John Phillips

All the leaves are brown   and the sky__ is grey.__

I've been for a walk   on a win-ter's day.__

1. I'd be safe and warm,____   if I was in L. A.____
2. If I did-n't tell her__   I could leave to-day.____

Ca - li - for - nia dream-in'____   on such a win-ter's

day.____   Stopped in-to a church   I passed a-long the

Candle In The Wind

Words & Music by Elton John & Bernie Taupin

Moderately slow, in 2

Verse

Strum pattern

1. Good - bye, Nor - ma Jean.____ Though I nev - er knew you at all,____

(Verses 2–3 see block lyric)

____ you had the grace to hold your - self____ while those a - round____ you crawled.____

They crawled out of the wood - work____ and they whis - pered in - to____ your brain;

____ they set you on a tread - mill and they made you change____ your name.____

Chorus

And it seems to me____ you lived your life____ like a

can - dle in___ the wind,_____ nev - er know - ing who to

cling to when the rain set in.___ And I

would have liked__ to have known you, but I was just a kid.___ Your

can - dle burned__ out long be - fore___ your leg - end ev - er did._____

1. 2. / **3.**

Your can - dle burned__ out

long be - fore___ your leg - end ev - er did._____

Verse 2:   Loneliness was tough, the toughest role you ever played
Hollywood created a superstar and pain was the price you paid
Even when you died the press still hounded you
All the papers had to say was that Marilyn was found in the nude.
Chorus

Verse 3:   Goodbye, Norma Jean. Though I never knew you at all
You had the grace to hold yourself while those around you crawled
Goodbye, Norma Jean, from the young man in the twenty-second row
Who sees you as something more than sexual, more than just our Marilyn Monroe.
Chorus

C'mon Everybody

Words & Music by Eddie Cochran & Jerry Capehart

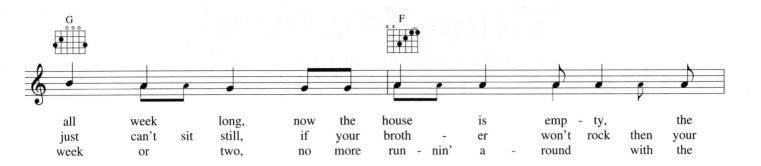

all   week   long,   now the house   is   emp - ty,   the
just can't sit   still,   if your broth - er   won't rock then your
week   or   two,   no more run - nin' a - round with the

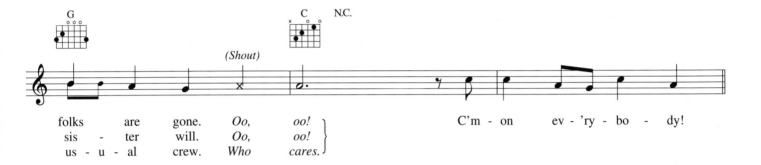

(Shout)

folks   are   gone.   *Oo,*   *oo!*   C'm - on ev -'ry - bo - dy!
sis - ter   will.   *Oo,*   *oo!*
us - u - al crew.   *Who* *cares.*

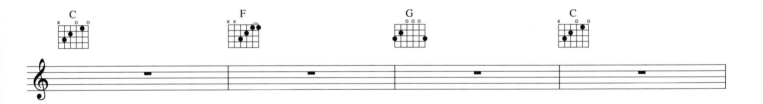

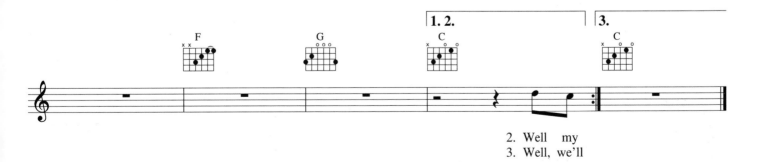

2. Well my
3. Well, we'll

Crocodile Rock

Words & Music by Elton John & Bernie Taupin

clock, ___ we were hop - pin' and bop - pin' to the Croc - o - dile Rock. Well,

Croc - o - dile Rock - in' is some - thing shock - in' when your

feet just can't keep still. ___ I nev - er knew me a

bet - ter time ___ and I guess ___ I ne - ver will. ___

Oh! Law - dy ma - ma, those Fri - day nights ___ when Su - sie wore ___ her

dress - es tight ___ and the Croc - o - dile Rock - in' was

out ___ of ___ sight. ___

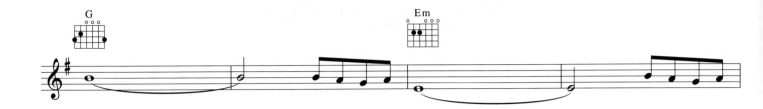

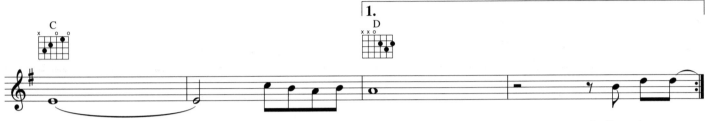

2. But the years___

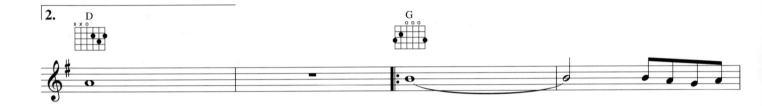

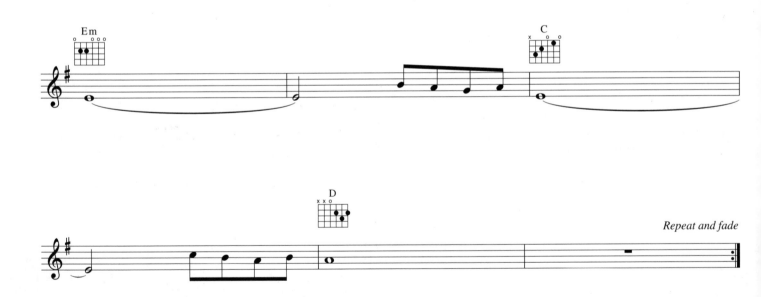

Repeat and fade

Verse 2:

But the years went by and rock just died
Susie went and left me for some foreign guy
Long nights cryin' by the record machine
Dreamin' of my Chevy and my old blue jeans
But they'll never kill the thrills we've got
Burning up to the Crocodile Rock
Learning fast as the weeks went past
We really thought the Crocodile Rock would last.
Chorus

Disco 2000

Music by Pulp. Lyrics by Jarvis Cocker

1. Well we were born with-in an hour of each oth-er, our moth-ers
(Verse 2 see block lyric)

said we could be sis-ter and broth-er, your name is De-bo-rah, De-bo-rah,

it nev-er suit-ed ya. And they

said that when we grew up, we'd get mar-ried and nev-er split up,

Verse 2:

You were the first girl at school to get breasts
Martyn said that yours were the best
The boys all loved you but I was a mess
I had to watch them trying to get you undressed
We were friends but that was as far as it went
I used to walk you home sometimes but
It meant nothing to you
'Cause you were so popular.

Da Ya Think I'm Sexy?

Words & Music by Rod Stewart & Carmine Appice

Moderately

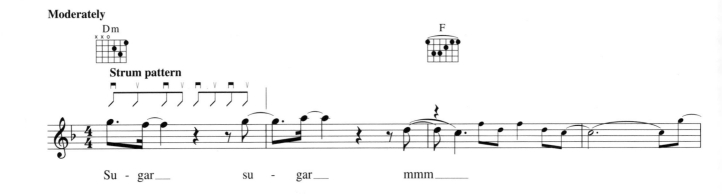

Su - gar ___ su - gar ___ mmm ___

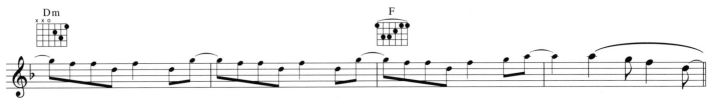

ooh. ___

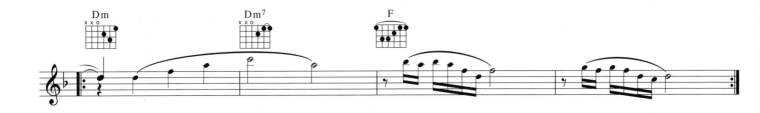

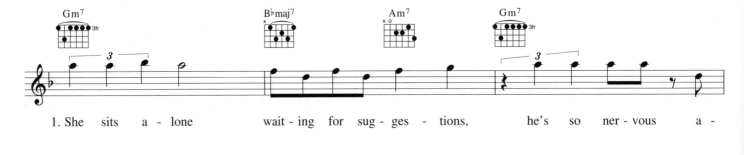

1. She sits a - lone wait - ing for sug - ges - tions, he's so ner - vous a -

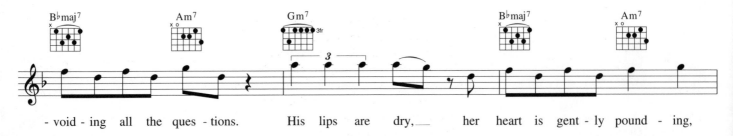

-void - ing all the ques - tions. His lips are dry, ___ her heart is gent - ly pound - ing,

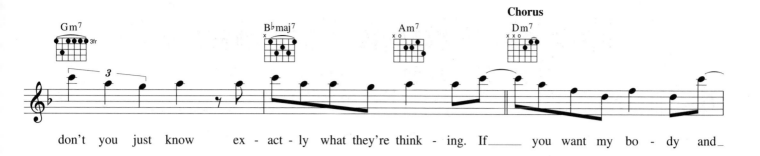

don't you just know ex - act - ly what they're think - ing. If_____ you want my bo - dy and__

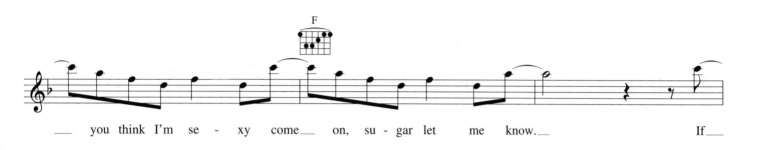

__ you think I'm se - xy come__ on, su - gar let me know.__ If__

__ you real - ly need me just__ reach out and touch me, come__ on ho - ney tell me so.__

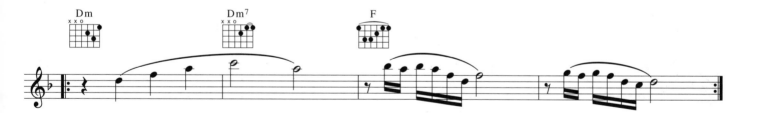

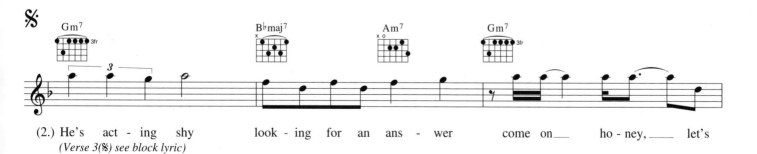

(2.) He's act - ing shy look - ing for an ans - wer come on__ ho - ney,__ let's
(Verse 3(%) see block lyric)

47

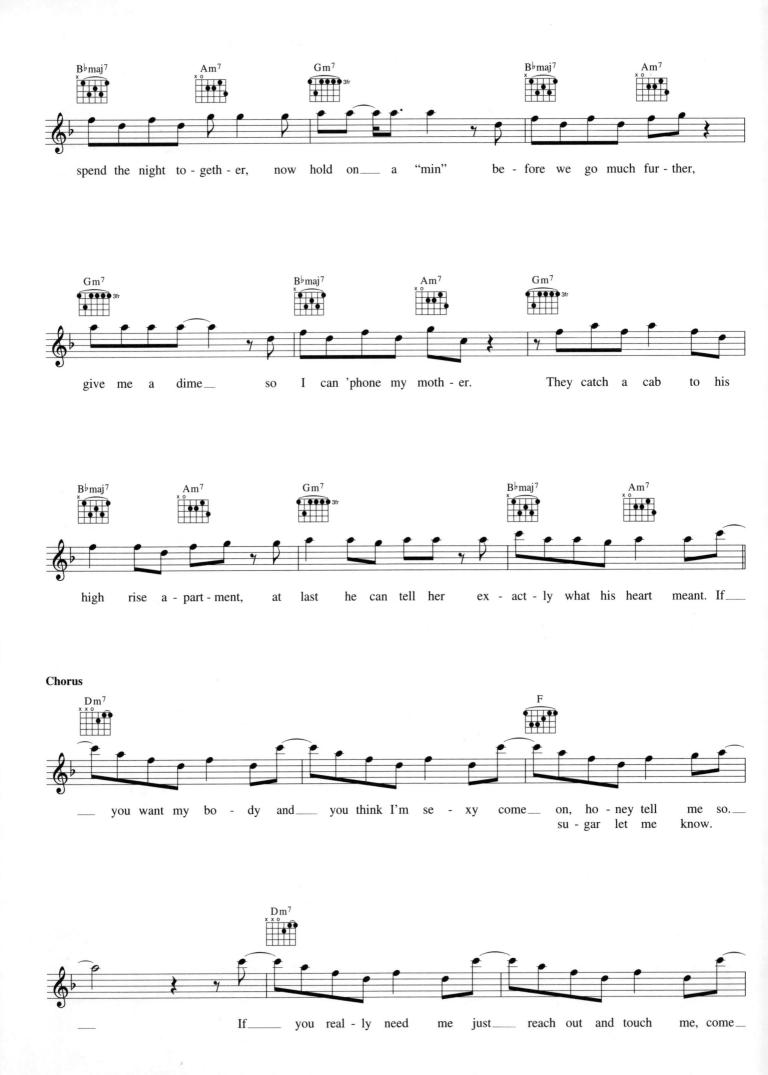

Instrumental

_ on su - gar let me know._
ho - ney, tell me so._

(His) heart's beat - ing like a drum_

_ 'cos at last he's got this girl home._

D. %
(Repeat instrumental section ad lib to fade)

Re - lax ba - by now we're all a - lone._

Verse 3(%): They wake at dawn 'cos all the birds are singing
Two total strangers but that ain't what they're thinking
Outside it's cold misty and it's raining
They got each other, neither one's complaining
He says I'm sorry but I'm out of milk and coffee
Never mind sugar, we can watch the early movie.

Easy Lover

Music by Phil Collins, Philip Bailey & Nathan East. Words by Phil Collins

Youʼll___ nev - er get it.___ She will play___
Youʼll___ nev - er get it.___ ʼCause sheʼll say___

___ a - round and leave you, leave___ you and de - ceive you.
___ that thereʼs no oth - er till___ she finds an - oth - er.

Bet - ter for - get___ it. Oh,___ youʼll re -
Bet - ter for - get___ it. Oh,___ youʼll re -

- gret it.___ No, youʼll nev - er change her, so
- gret it.___ And donʼt try to change her. Just

leave her, leave her. Get out quick ʼcause see - ing is be - liev - ing. } Itʼs the
leave her, leave her. Youʼre not on - one, see - ing is be - liev - ing.

on - ly way___ youʼll ev - er know.___

D. $ and fade

Sheʼs an ea - sy lov - ___ an eas - y lov -

51

Every Little Thing
She Does Is Magic

Words & Music by Sting

Though I've tried be - fore____ to tell____ her of the feel -
have to tell____ the stor - y of a thou -

- ings I have for her in____ my_____ heart____
- sand rain - y days____ since we first____ met.____

ev - 'ry time____
get - ting wet.

____ that I____ come near____ her I____ just lose____ my nerve____ as I've____ done from the start.
____ en - ough____ um - brel - la but____ it's al - ways me____ that ends____ up get - ting wet.

Ev - 'ry lit - tle thing she does____ is mag - ic, ev - 'ry - thing she

do just turns____ me on,____ ev - en though my life be - fore____ was trag - ic, now I know my

52

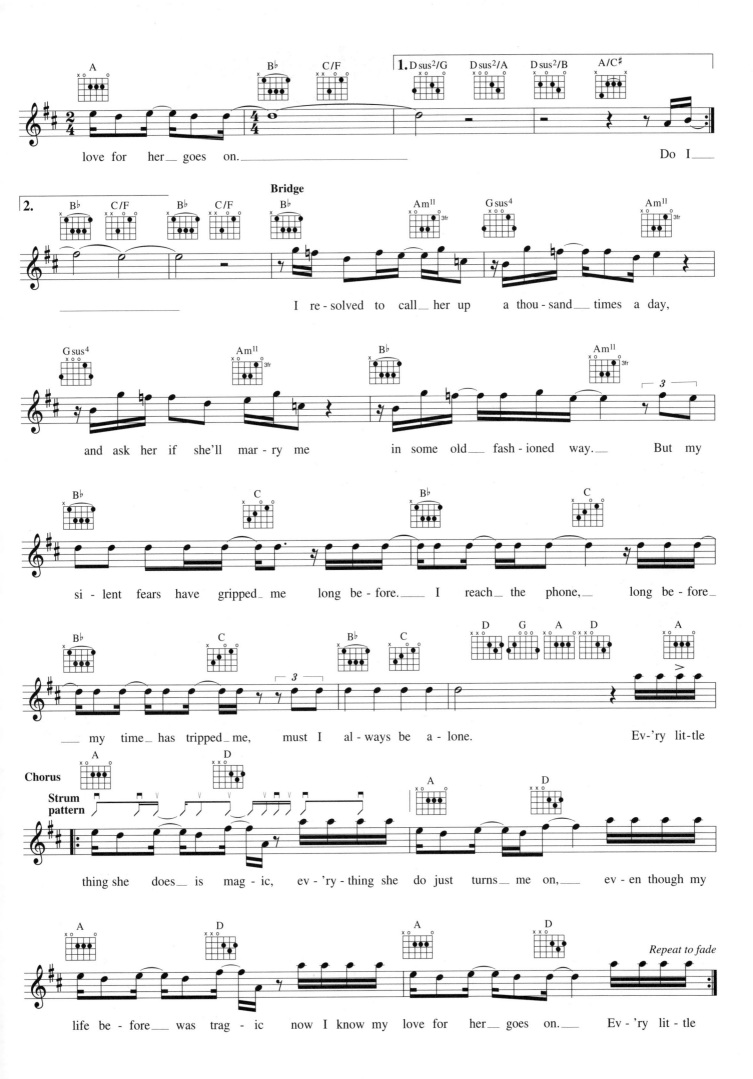

Exodus

Words & Music by Bob Marley

Moderate reggae

Ex - o - dus, ___ move - ment of Jah peo-

- ple, oh ___ yeah. ___ O - pen your eyes and let me tell you this.

Men and peo - ple will fight ya down *Spoken: Tell me why* when you see ___ Jah light. ___
(2,3.) O - pen your eyes, and look with - in. ___

Let me tell you, if you're not wrong, *Spoken: Then why?* ev - 'ry - thing is al - right. So we gon - na
Are you sat - is - fied

walk, al - right, ___ through the roads ___ of cre - a - tion.
We know where ___ we're go - ing. We know where ___ we're from. ___ We're

We're the gen - er - a - tion *Spoken: Tell me why!* trod through great trib - u - la - tion.
leav - ing Bab - y - lon, we're go - ing to our to our fath - er - land.

Ex - o - dus,___   Move - ment   of   Jah peo -

To Coda ✛ |1.

- ple.

|2.   D.% |3.

(Move - ment   of   Jah peo - ple.)   (Move - ment   of   Jah peo -
Send   us   an - oth - er   Broth - er   Mos - es.

                                                     |1.

- ple.)   (Move - ment   of   Jah peo - ple.)   Send   us   an - oth - er   Broth - er
Gon - na   cross___ the Red___ Sea._____

|2.

- ple.)   Ex - o - dus,___   Move - ment   of   Jah peo -

- ple.

Ex - o - dus,___   Ex - o - dus,___   Move!

Play 4 times

D. %: al Coda ⊕

1.2.   **3.**

Move!

Coda ⊕

Move - ment of Jah peo - ple;   move - ment of Jah peo -

- ple.   Jah come to break down 'pres - sion,   rule e - qual - i - ty,

wipe a - way trans - gres - sion,   set the cap - tives free.___

___   Ex - o - dus,___   move - ment of Jah peo -

Repeat to fade

- ple.   Move - ment of Jah peo - ple;

15 Years

Words & Music by Simon Friend, Charles Heather, Mark Chadwick, Jonathan Sevink & Jeremy Cunningham

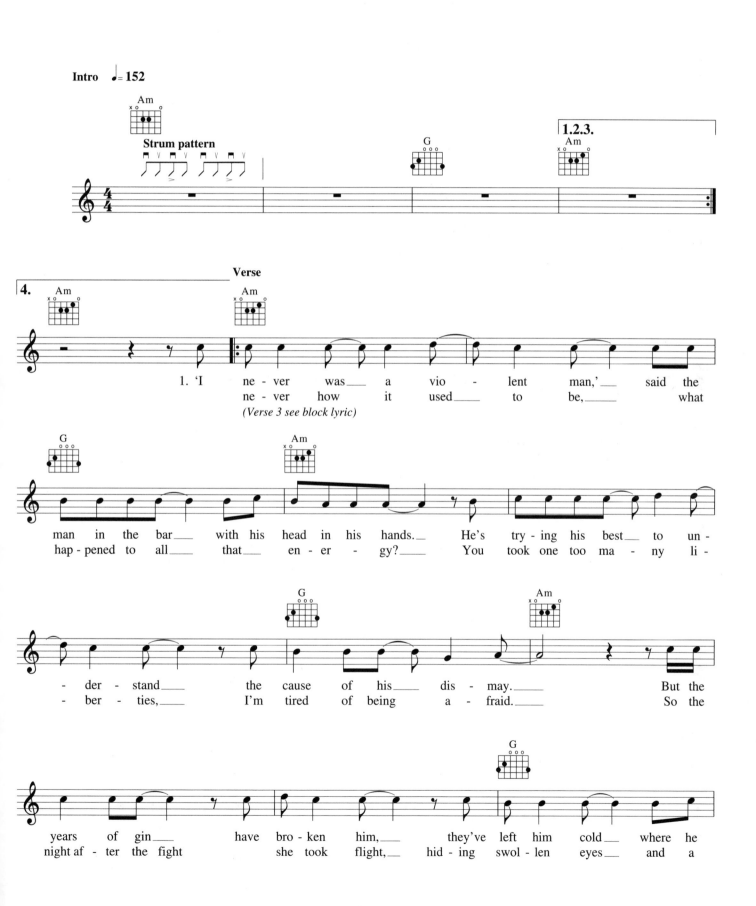

fit - ted   in.____   But   it's   too   late____   now   to   turn a - round____   and
woun - ded   pride,____   the   best   years   of____ her   life____ de - nied,____   and

find   an - oth - er   way.____   And   the   laughs   in   the   late   night
sold   for   li - quid   shares.____

lock - in   are   fad - ing   a - way____   when   he   gets   in,____   the

girl   from fif - teen   years   a - go____   has   packed   and   gone a - way.____

1. cont.

(Instrumental)

1. cont.

2. That's ____   And the

Middle

2. cont.

vic - tims   of ____ their   world ____   are   ad - ver - tised ____ on   post -

58

Verse 3:

It's another week till his cheque comes through
He's got a fiver left now to spend on food
But the doors of the bar are open
And he breaks another rule
Well he sits on the stool that bears his name
He's got a favourite glass that's called the same
He's never been kept waiting
'Cos he pays the landlord's wage.

Fifty Ways To Leave Your Lover

Words & Music by Paul Simon

fif - ty ways to leave your lov - er, fif - ty ways to leave your
fif - ty ways to leave your lov - er, fif - ty ways to leave your

Chorus

lov - er." Just slip out the back, Jack; make a new plan, Stan;
lov - er."

you don't need to be coy, Roy; { just get your - self free.
                                        { just lis - ten to me.

Hop on the bus, Gus; you don't need to dis - cuss___

___ much;_____ just drop off the key, Lee,

To Coda ⊕ **1.**

and get your - self free. Slip out the

D.C. *(with repeats)* **al Coda** ⊕   ⊕ **Coda**

2.

free.   free.

Get It On (Bang A Gong)

Words & Music by Marc Bolan

get it on.

Well you're built___ like a car___ you've got a hub cap dia - mond star ha -

- lo,___ You're built like a truck,___ oh yeah.

You're an un - tanned youth, that's the truth___ with your cloak___ full of ea -

- gles,_____ you're dir - ty sweet and you're my girl.

⊕ Coda

D. %. al Coda ⊕

Get it on,___

Get it on._____

Gimme All Your Lovin'

Words & Music by Billy Gibbons, Dusty Hill & Frank Beard

1. I got to have a shot
(Verses 2&3 see block lyric)
'cause

what you got is oh so sweet_____ you got to make it hot_____

like a boom-e-rang I need a re-peat._____

Gim-me all your lov-in' all your hugs and kiss-es too.

Gim - me   all   your   lo - vin'_____   don't let   up   un - til   we're   through__

1.

2.3.   Solo   To Coda ⊕

2. You   got   to

1.   **2.**   D. 𝄊 al Coda ⊕

3. You   got   to

⊕ Coda

Solo

Repeat to fade

Verse 2:   You got to whip it up
And hit me like a ton of lead
If I blow my top
Will you let it go to your head?

Verse 3:   You got to move it up
And use it like a screwball would
You got to pack it up
Work it like a new boy should.

Have I Told You Lately?

Words & Music by Van Morrison

© Copyright 1989 Essential Music.
PolyGram Music Publishing Limited, 47 British Grove, London W4.
All Rights Reserved. International Copyright Secured.

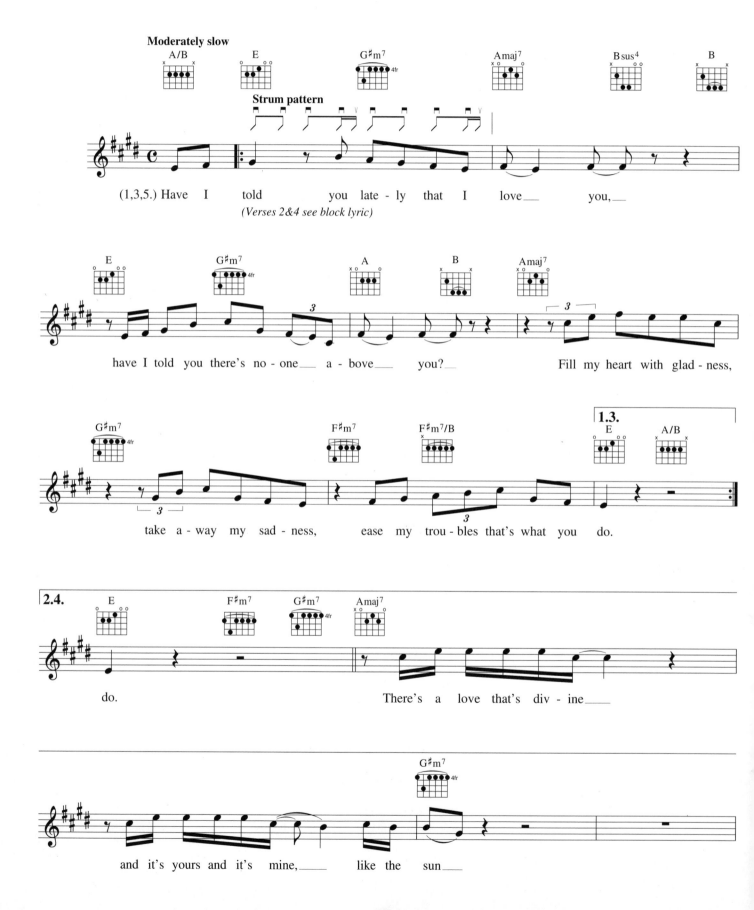

(1,3,5.) Have I told you late - ly that I love___ you,___

(Verses 2&4 see block lyric)

have I told you there's no - one___ a - bove___ you?___ Fill my heart with glad - ness,

take a - way my sad - ness, ease my trou - bles that's what you do.

do. There's a love that's div - ine___

and it's yours and it's mine,___ like the sun___

Verse 2:   Oh the morning sun in all its glory
            Greets the day with hope and comfort too
            And you fill my life with laughter
            You can make it better
            Ease my troubles that's what you do.

Verse 3:   as Verse 1

Verse 4:   instrumental

Middle: There's a love that's divine
            And it's yours and it's mine
            And it shines like the sun
            At the end of the day
            We will give thanks and pray to the one.

Verse 5:   as Verse 1

Hey Jude

Words & Music by John Lennon & Paul McCartney

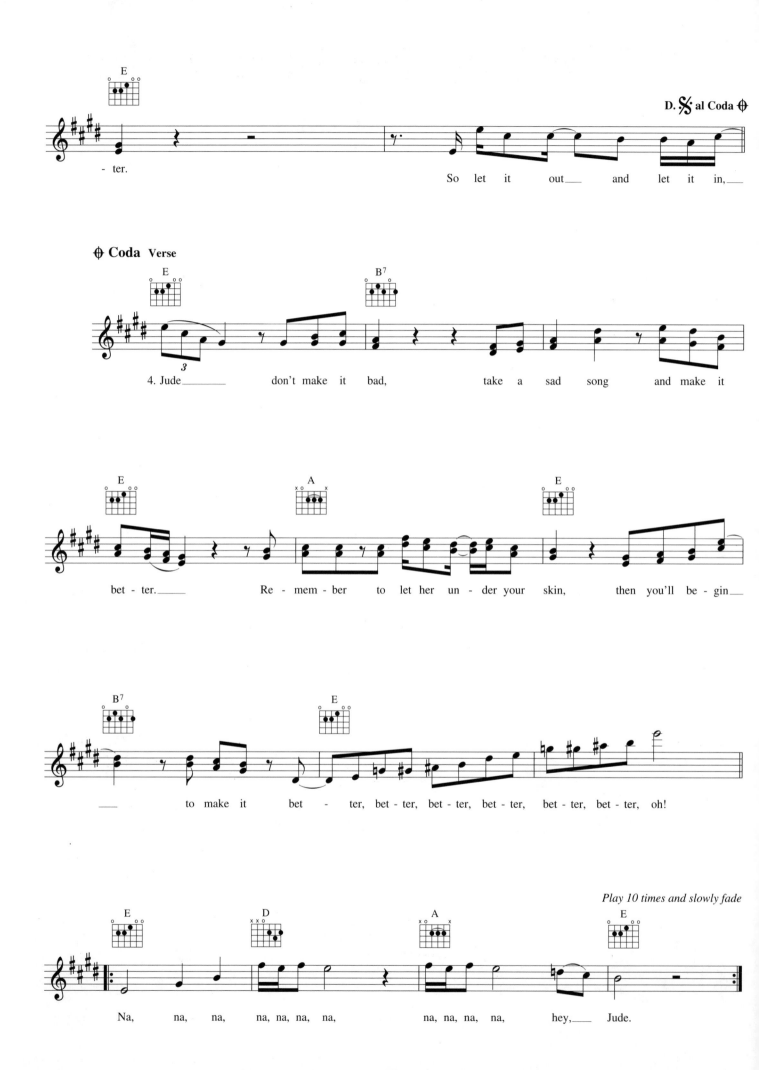

If I Ever Lose My Faith In You

Words & Music by Sting

1. You could say I lost my faith in sci-ence and pro-gress.
(Verses 2–3 see block lyric)

You could say I lost my be-lief in the ho-ly church.

You could say I lost my sense of di-rec-

-tion, yes, you could say all of this and worse. But

if I ev-er lose my faith in you,

there'd be no-thing left___ for__ me__ to do.___

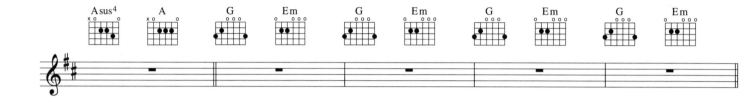

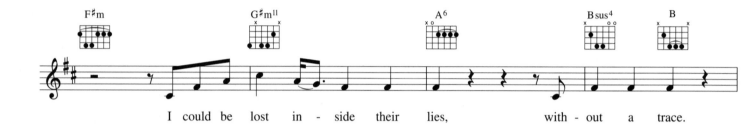

I could be lost in - side their lies, with - out a trace.

D.C. al Coda ⊕

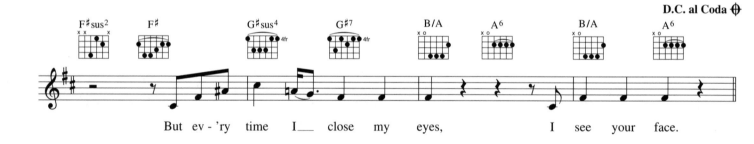

But ev - 'ry time I___ close my eyes, I see your face.

⊕ **Coda**

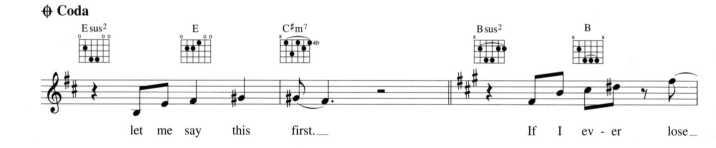

let me say this first.___ If I ev - er lose___

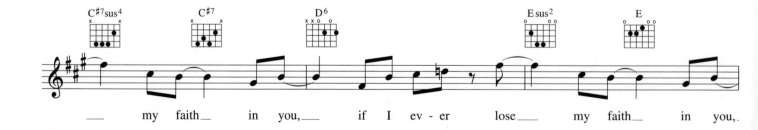

___ my faith___ in you,___ if I ev - er lose___ my faith___ in you,

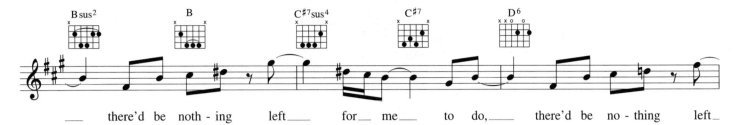

there'd be noth - ing left___ for___ me___ to do,___ there'd be no - thing left___

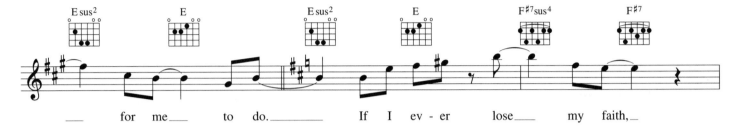

for me___ to do.___ If I ev - er lose___ my faith,___

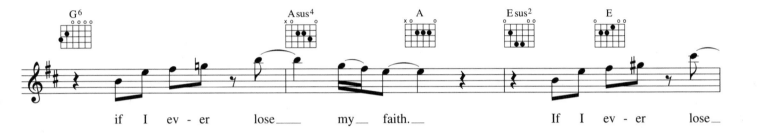

if I ev - er lose___ my___ faith.___ If I ev - er lose___

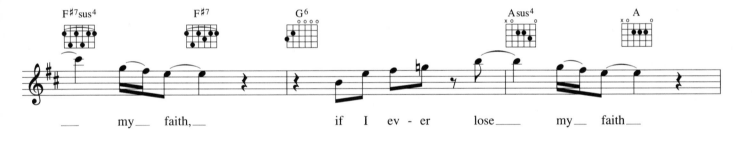

___ my___ faith,___ if I ev - er lose___ my___ faith___

Repeat to fade

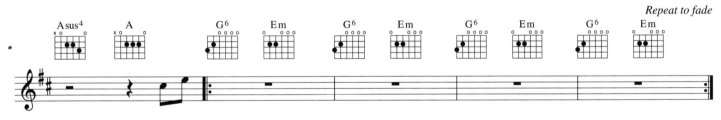

in you.

Verse 2:   Some would say I was a lost man in a lost world
You could say I lost my faith in the people on T.V.
You could say I lost my faith in our politicians
They all seem like game show hosts to me.

Verse 3:   I never saw no miracle of science
That didn't go from a blessing to a curse
I never saw no military solution
That didn't always end up as something worse but
Let me say this first.
(To Coda)

I Will

Words & Music by John Lennon & Paul McCartney

Imagine

Words & Music by John Lennon

I - ma - gine there's no hea - ven, it's ea - sy if you

try,_____ no hell__ be - low__ us,

a - bove us on - ly sky. I - ma - gine all the peo -

- ple__ liv - ing for to - day,___ a - ha.___

I - ma - gine there's no coun - tries,___ It is - n't hard to do,_
I - ma - gine no pos - ses - sions,___ I won - der if you can,

In The City

Words & Music by Paul Weller

In the ci - ty there's a thou - sand things_ I wan - na
In the ci - ty there's a thou - sand fa - ces all
In the ci - ty there's a thou - sand men ___ in

say to you._ But when - ev - er I ap -
shin - ing bright._ And those gol - den
un - i - forms.___ And I've heard they now

- proach you, you make me look a fool._
fa - ces are un - der twen - ty five._
have the right to kill a man.___

I wan - na say,___ I wan - na tell
They wan - na say,___ They're gon - na tell
We wan - na say,___ We're gon - na tell_

you a - bout the young i - dea. But you
you a - bout the young i - dea. You bet - ter
you a - bout the young i - dea. And if it

turn them in - to fears.
listen now you've said your bit.
don't work at least we tried.

I don't know what you're think - ing, you still think I am crap.

But you'd bet - ter lis - ten man be - cause the

kids know where it's at.

79

Instant Karma

Words & Music by John Lennon

In - stant Kar - ma's gon - na get you,
In - stant Kar - ma's gon - na get you,

gon - na tap you right on the head!___
gon - na knock you right in the face!___

You bet - ter get your - self to - geth - er.___ Pret - ty soon you're gon - na be dead!
You bet - ter get your - self to - geth - er.___ Join the hu - man race!

___ What in the world are you think - ing of?
How in the world are you gon - na see?

Just Can't Get Enough

Words & Music by Vincent Clarke

(1.) When I'm with you, ba - by, I go out__ of my head,
2. We walk to - geth - er, walk - ing down__ the street, and I
3. And when it rains,__ you're shin - ing down__ for me,__

just can't get e - nough,__ and I just can't get e - nough.__

All the things__ you do to me__ and ev - 'ry - thing you said,__ I
Ev - 'ry time I think of you__ I know we have to meet,__ and I
just like a rain - bow__ you know you set me free,__ and I

just can't get e - nough,__ I just can't get e - nough.__

We slip and slide as we fall in love,__ and I
It's get - ting hard - er, it's a burn - ing love,__ and I
you're like an an - gel and you give me your love,__ and I

just can't seem to get e - nough of...

1.

2.

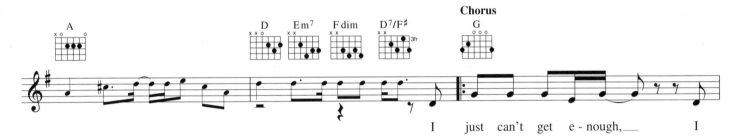

Chorus

I just can't get e - nough, ___ I

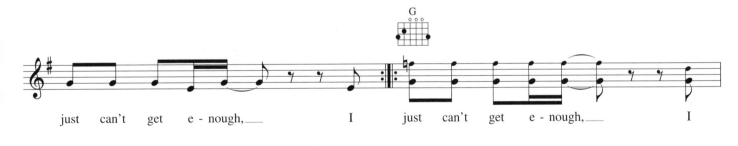

just can't get e - nough, ___ I just can't get e - nough, ___ I

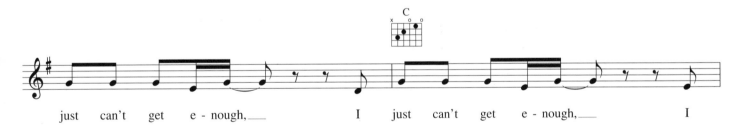

just can't get e - nough, ___ I just can't get e - nough, ___ I

D.C. *take 2° bar and fade ad lib on Chorus*

just can't get e - nough, ___ I just can't get e - nough, ___ I just can't get e - nough, ___ (I)

(omit on D.C.)

Keep The Faith

Words & Music by Jon Bon Jovi, Richie Sambora & Desmond Child

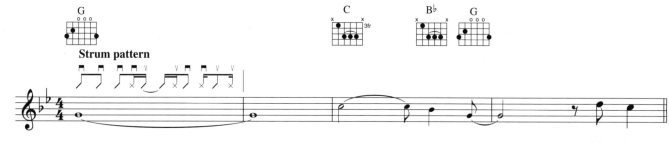

1. Mo - ther,

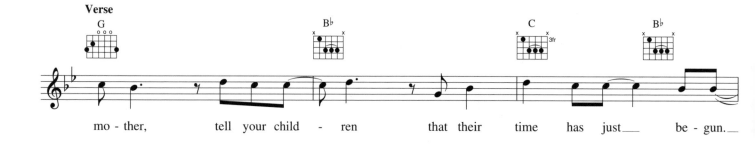

mo - ther, tell your child - ren that their time has just___ be - gun.___

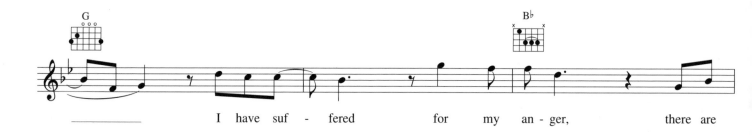

I have suf - fered for my an - ger, there are

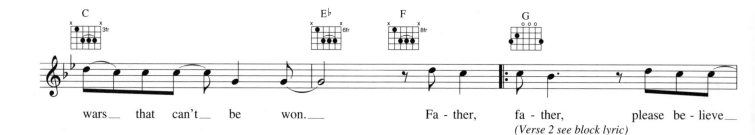

wars___ that can't___ be won.___ Fa - ther, fa - ther, please be - lieve___

(Verse 2 see block lyric)

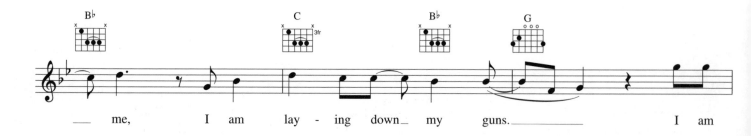

___ me, I am lay - ing down___ my guns.___ I am

bro - ken _____ like an ar - row. _____ For - give me, for -

- give your way - ward son. Ev - 'ry - bo - dy needs some - bo - dy to love, _ ev -
(See Block Lyrics on 𝄋)

- 'ry - bo - dy needs some - bo - dy to hate. _ Ev - 'ry - bo - dy's bitch - ing 'cause they

can't get e - nough, _ and it's hard _ to hold on _ when there's no -

Chorus

- one to lean _ on. Faith, you know you're gon - na live through the rain, _
(Chorus 2 see block lyric)

_ Lord, _ you got to keep the faith. _ Faith,

85

Lord,__ we got to keep the faith,_____

Guitar Solo

yeah, yeah, yeah. I've been

walk - ing in the foot - steps of so - ci - e - ty's lies,__ I don't

like what I see no more, I some - times wish I was blind. Some -

- times I wait for - ev - er to stand out in__ the rain,__ so

D. % al Coda ⊕

no - one sees me cry - ing, try - ing to wash a - way this pain 3. Mo - ther fa - (ther)

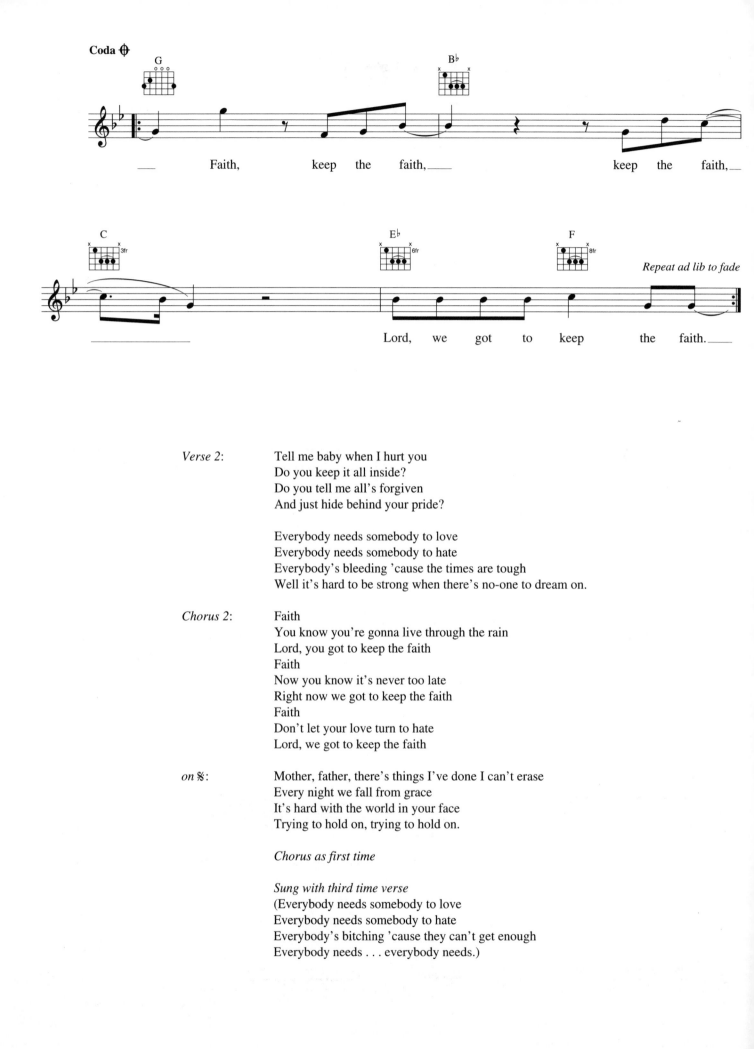

Coda ⊕

Faith, keep the faith,___ keep the faith,___

___ Lord, we got to keep the faith.___

Repeat ad lib to fade

Verse 2:
Tell me baby when I hurt you
Do you keep it all inside?
Do you tell me all's forgiven
And just hide behind your pride?

Everybody needs somebody to love
Everybody needs somebody to hate
Everybody's bleeding 'cause the times are tough
Well it's hard to be strong when there's no-one to dream on.

Chorus 2:
Faith
You know you're gonna live through the rain
Lord, you got to keep the faith
Faith
Now you know it's never too late
Right now we got to keep the faith
Faith
Don't let your love turn to hate
Lord, we got to keep the faith

on 𝄋:
Mother, father, there's things I've done I can't erase
Every night we fall from grace
It's hard with the world in your face
Trying to hold on, trying to hold on.

Chorus as first time

Sung with third time verse
(Everybody needs somebody to love
Everybody needs somebody to hate
Everybody's bitching 'cause they can't get enough
Everybody needs . . . everybody needs.)

Linger

Music by Dolores O'Riordan & Noel Hogan. Words by Dolores O'Riordan

Verse

I swore I would be true____ and hon-ey, so did you,____ so
if you could get by____ try-ing not to lie,____

why____ were you hold-ing____ her hand?____ Is that the way____ we stand?
things would-n't be so____ con-fused,____ and I would-n't feel so used,

____ Were you ly-ing all____ the time?____ Was it just a game____ to you?
____ but you al-ways real-ly knew____ I just wan-na be____ with you.

𝄋 Chorus

____ But I'm in____ so deep, you know I'm such a fool____ for you,

you got me wrapped a-round your fin-ger,____ ah,____ ah,____ ha. Do you have to let it lin-

Middle 8

To Coda ⊕

- ger? Do you have to, do you have to, do you have to let it lin- ger?____

(2° Instrumental solo)

Oh, I thought the world_ of you,____ I thought noth-ing could_ go wrong,

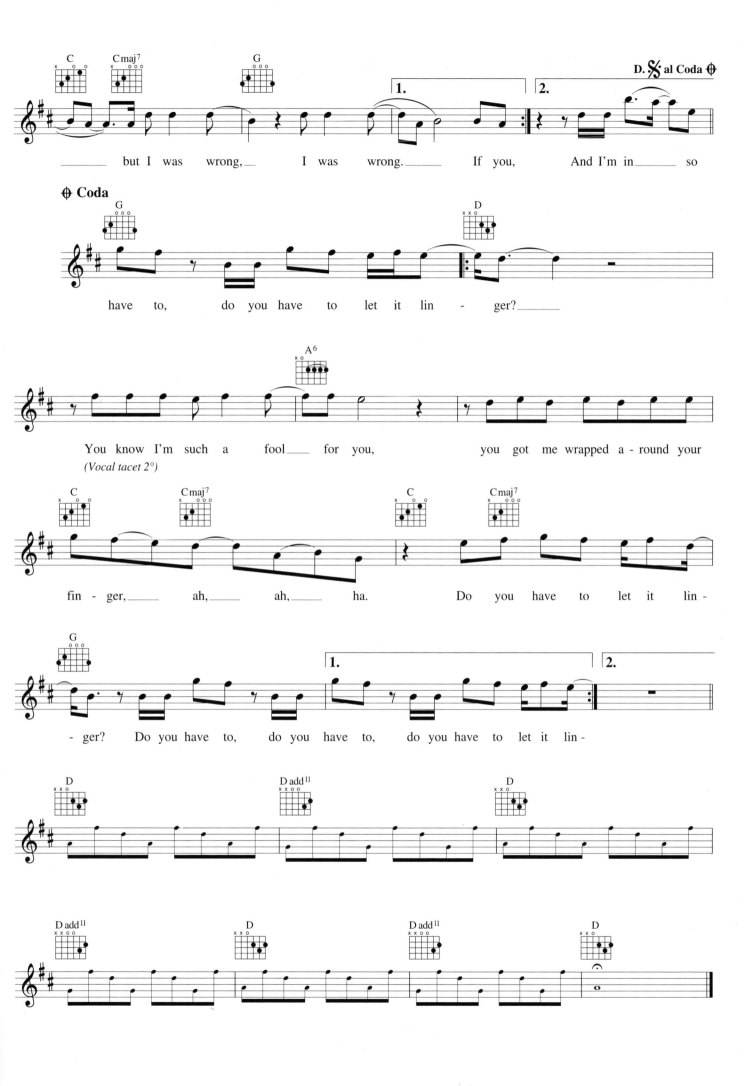

Me And Julio Down By The Schoolyard

Words & Music by Paul Simon

saw,   it was a - gainst the law.___   The

ma - ma looked down and spit on the ground ev - 'ry
cou - ple of days they come and take me a - way but the

time my names___ gets men - tioned,   the
press let the sto - ry leak,_____   and when the

pa - pa said, "Oy, if I get that boy___ I'm gon - na
ra - di - cal priest come to get me re - leased we's

stick him in the house of de - ten - tion."   Well, I'm on my
all on the cov - er of News - week.

way,   I don't know where I'm go - in',_____ I'm on my

93

Missing

Music by Ben Watt. Words by Tracey Thorn

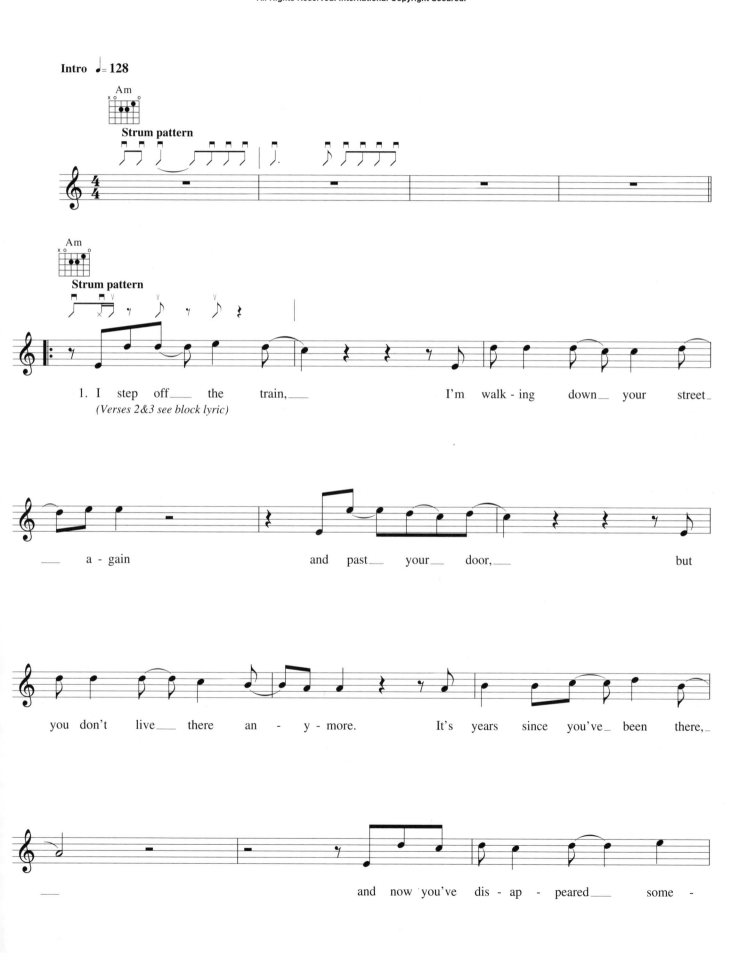

1. I step off the train, I'm walking down your street
(Verses 2&3 see block lyric)

a - gain and past your door, but

you don't live there an - y - more. It's years since you've been there,

and now you've dis - ap - peared some -

Verse 2:   Could you be dead?
You always were two steps ahead of everyone
We'd walk behind while you would run
I look up at your house
And I can almost hear you shout down to me
Where I always used to be
And I miss you.

Verse 3:   Back on the train
I ask why did I come again?
Can I confess I've been hanging 'round your old address
And the years have proved
To offer nothing since you moved
You're long gone but I can't move on
And I miss you.

97

Mrs Robinson

Words & Music by Paul Simon

And here's to you.___ Mrs___ Rob - in - son,___

Je - sus loves you more___ than you___ will know._____ Wo, wo, wo.__

___ God bless you please,__ Mrs__ Rob - in - son,__

hea - ven holds a place__ for those__ who pray._____ Hey, hey, hey,_

_____ hey, hey, hey.__ We'd like to know_ a lit-

- tle bit__ a - bout__ you for__ our files._____ We'd

D⁷   G

like to help__ you learn to help your - self._____ Look a - round you all__

C   F   Dm

__ you see__ are sym - pa - the - tic eyes._____

A   G⁷   D. 𝄋 al Coda 𝄌

Stroll a - round__ the grounds__ un - til you feel at home.__ And here's to you,__

𝄌 Coda   A

Hide it in a hid - ing place__ where
Sit - ting on a so - fa on__ a

                A⁷   D⁷

no - one ev - er goes,_____ put it in your pan-
Sun - day af - ter - noon,_____ go - ing to the can-

                                            G

- try with__ your cup__ cakes._____ It's a lit - tle sec-
- di - dates'__ de - bate.____ Laugh a - bout it, shout

99

My Father's Eyes

Words & Music by Eric Clapton

1. Sail - in' down be - hind the sun, wait - in' for ___ the prince ___ to come. ___

(Verses 2&3 see block lyric)

Pray - in'___ for___ the heal - in' rain to re - store___ my soul a - gain.___

Just a tour - ing, on___ the___ run. And how did I get here?

What___ have I done?___ When will all___ my___ hopes___ sur - mise?

To Coda $\oplus$ **Chorus**

And how will I know him when I look in___ my fa - ther's eyes?_____

(Look in - to my fa-

My fa - ther's eyes.___ When I look in___ my fa - ther's eyes.___

- ther's eyes._) (Look in - to my fa-

1. **2.**

My fa - ther's eyes.___ _____

- ther's eyes._____)

102

Guitar Solo

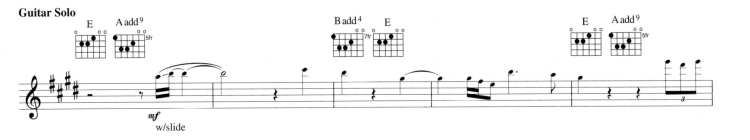

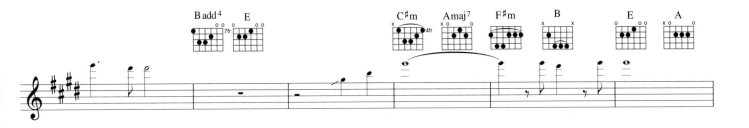

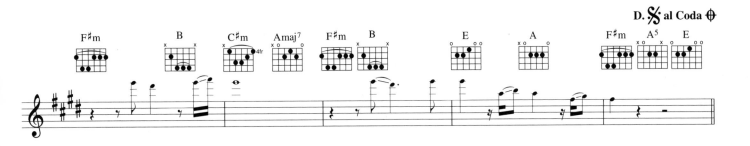

D. %. al Coda ⊕

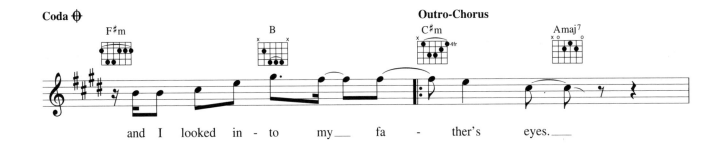

Coda ⊕

Outro-Chorus

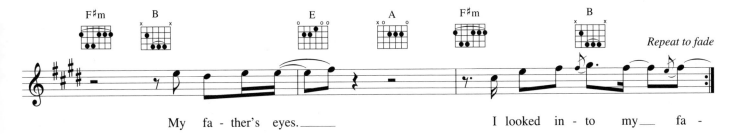

and I looked in - to my fa - ther's eyes.

Repeat to fade

My fa - ther's eyes. I looked in - to my fa -

Verse 2:
Then the light begins to shine
I hear those ancient lullabies
And as I watch the seedling grow
Feel my heart start to overflow.

Where do I find the words to say?
How do I teach him?
What do we play?
Bit by bit, I've realised
That's when I need them
That's when I need my father's eyes.

Verse 3:
Then the jagged edge appears
Through the distant clouds of tears
I'm like a bridge that was washed away
My foundation's one made of clay.

And as my soul slides down to die
How could I lose him?
What did I try?
Bit by bit, I've realised
That he was here with me
And I looked into my father's eyes.

Oh Boy

Words & Music by Sunny West, Bill Tilghman & Norman Petty

oh well, I

need you Peg - gy Sue.

Coda ⊕

Verse

4. I love you. Peg - gy Sue

rare and true, oh Peg - gy,

hue hue hue hue hue, oh well, I

want you Peg - gy Sue,

love you girl and I want you Peg - gy Sue.

Verse 2:
Peggy Sue, Peggy Sue
Oh, how my heart yearns for you
Oh, Peggy, my Peggy Sue
Oh well, I love you girl
Yes I love you Peggy Sue.

Verse 3(℅)

You can hear my heart call - in', A lit - tle bit o' lov - in' makes ev - 'ry - thing right, An'

I'm gon - na see my ba - by to - night! - ight! All o' my love, all o' my kiss - in'

You don't know what you been miss - in'! Oh Boy! (Oh Boy!) When you're with me, Oh Boy!

To Coda ⊕

(Oh Boy!) The world can see that you were meant for me.

Dum de dum dum, Oh Boy! Dum de dum dum, Oh Boy!

Ah, Ah, Ah,

D. %. al Coda ⊕ **Coda** ⊕

Ah, me.

Peggy Su[...]

Words & Music by Jerry Allison, Norman P[...]

Romeo And Juliet

Words & Music by Mark Knopfler

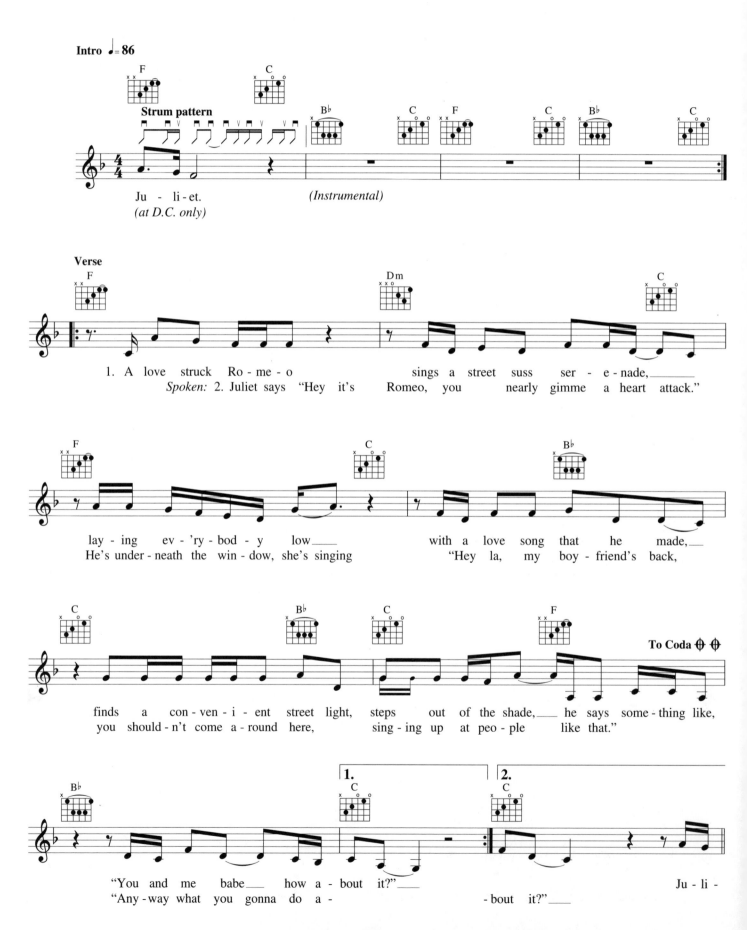

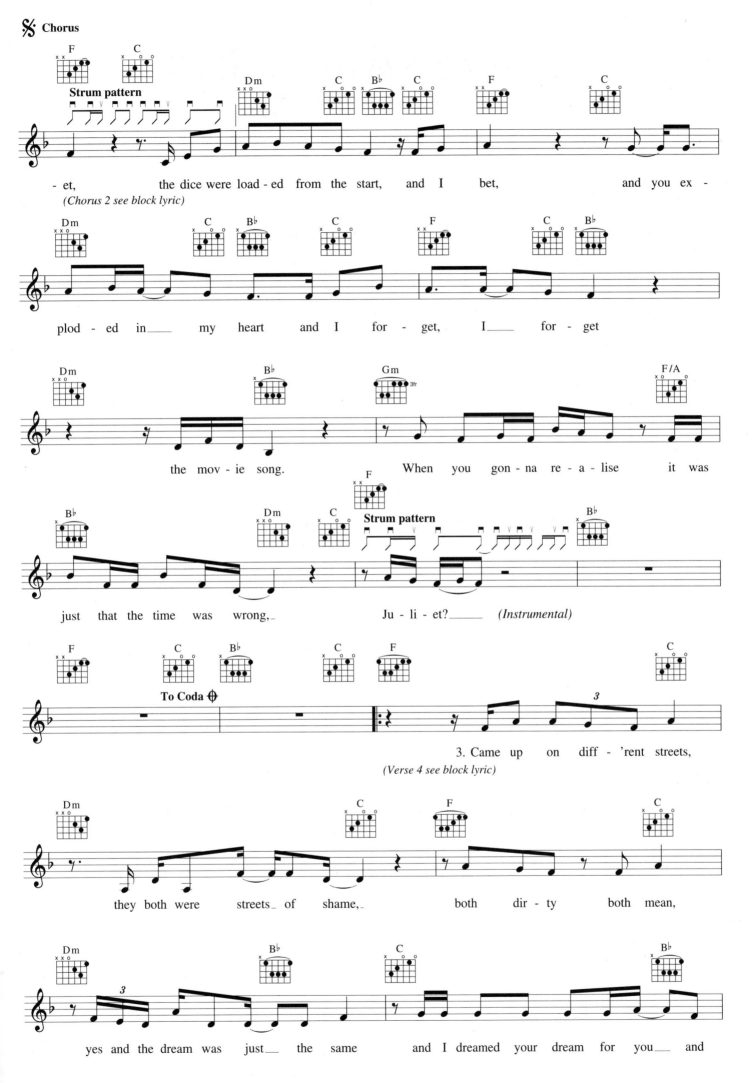

-et,   the dice were load-ed from the start,   and I   bet,   and you ex-

(Chorus 2 see block lyric)

plod-ed in___ my heart   and I   for - get,   I___   for - get

the mov-ie song.   When you gon-na re-a-lise   it was

just   that the time was   wrong,_   Ju-li-et?_____ *(Instrumental)*

To Coda

3. Came up   on diff-'rent streets,

(Verse 4 see block lyric)

they both were   streets_ of shame,_   both   dir-ty   both mean,

yes and the dream was just_ the same   and I dreamed your dream for you__ and

now your dream is real,___ how can you look at me as if I was

1.
just an-oth-er one of your deals. 4. When you can

2.
D. 𝄋 *(Chorus 2 lyrics)* **al Coda** ⊕
used to have a scene with him. Ju-li-

Coda ⊕
5. I can't_ do the talk___ like they talk on T. V.
6. And all I do is miss you and the way we used to be

and I can't do a love song like the way it's meant to be.
all I do is keep the beat and bad company,

I can't do ev-'ry-thing but I'd do an-y-thing for you,___
All I do is kiss you through the bars of a rhyme___

1.
I can't do an-y-thing except be in love___ with you.
Julie I'd do the stars with you

2.
Strum pattern
an-y-time.___ And Ju-li-et, when we made

110

love you used to cry, you said, "I love you like the stars a - bove, I'll

love you till__ I die." And there's a place___ for us, you know the mov - ie song,

D.C. al Coda ⊕⊕

when you gon - na re - a - lise it was just that the time was wrong,__

Coda ⊕⊕

Repeat ad lib to fade

you and me babe__ how a - bout it *Instrumental*

Verse 4:
Well you can fall for chains of silver,
You can fall for chains of gold
You can fall for pretty strangers
And the promises they hold
You promised me ev'rything
You promised me thick and thin
Now you just say "Oh Romeo, yeah,
You know I used to have a scene with him."

Chorus 2:
Juliet, when we made love you used to cry
You said "I love you like the stars above
I'll love you till I die
There's a place for us
You know the movie song"
When you gonna realise
It was just the time was wrong, Juliet?

Roxanne

Words & Music by Sting

Pride (In The Name Of Love)

Words & Music by U2

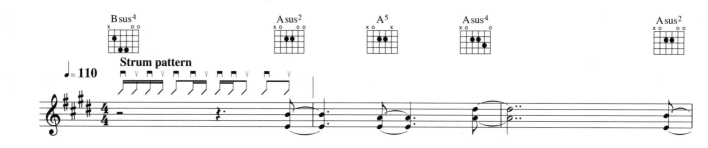

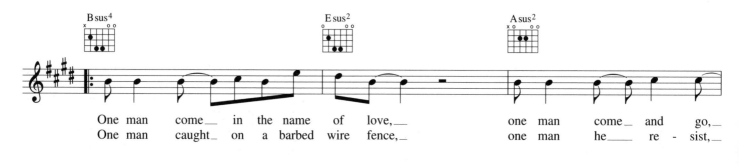

One man come in the name of love, one man come and go,

One man caught on a barbed wire fence, one man he resist,

one man come he to justify,

one man washed up on an empty beach,

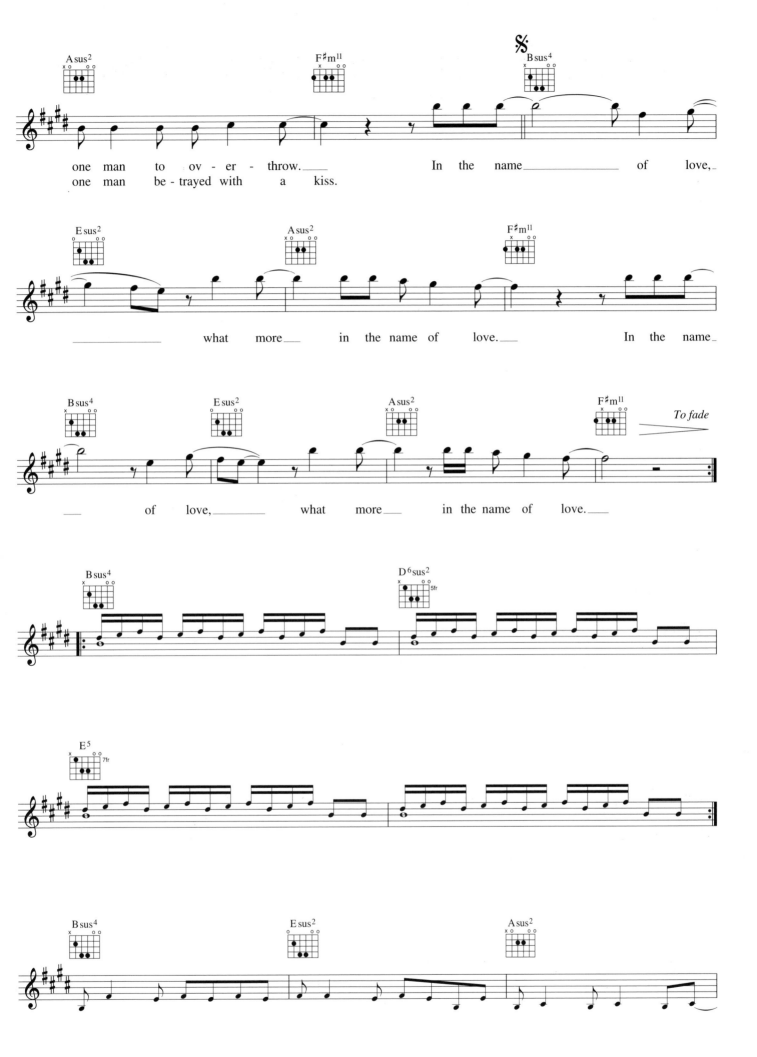

one man to ov - er - throw.___ In the name_____ of love,_

one man be - trayed with a kiss.

_____ what more___ in the name of love.___ In the name_

___ of love,_____ what more___ in the name of love.___

115

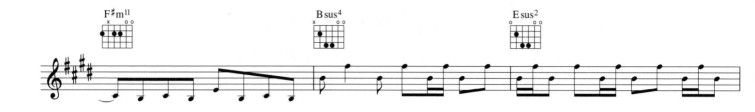

Mmm,_____ mmm,_

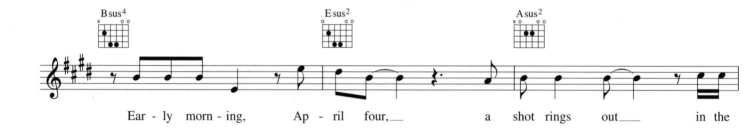

_____ mmm._____

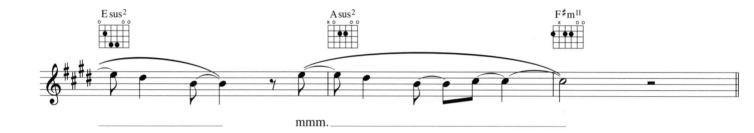

Ear - ly morn - ing, Ap - ril four,___ a shot rings out___ in the

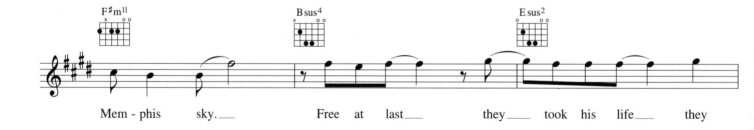

Mem - phis sky.___ Free at last___ they___ took his life___ they

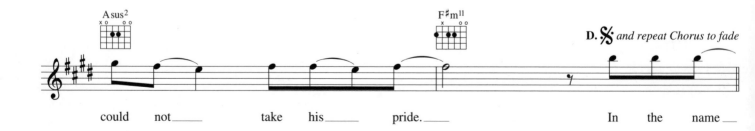

could not___ take his___ pride.___ In the name

D. 𝄋 *and repeat Chorus to fade*

116

She Loves You

Words & Music by John Lennon & Paul McCartney

So Lonely

Words & Music by Sting

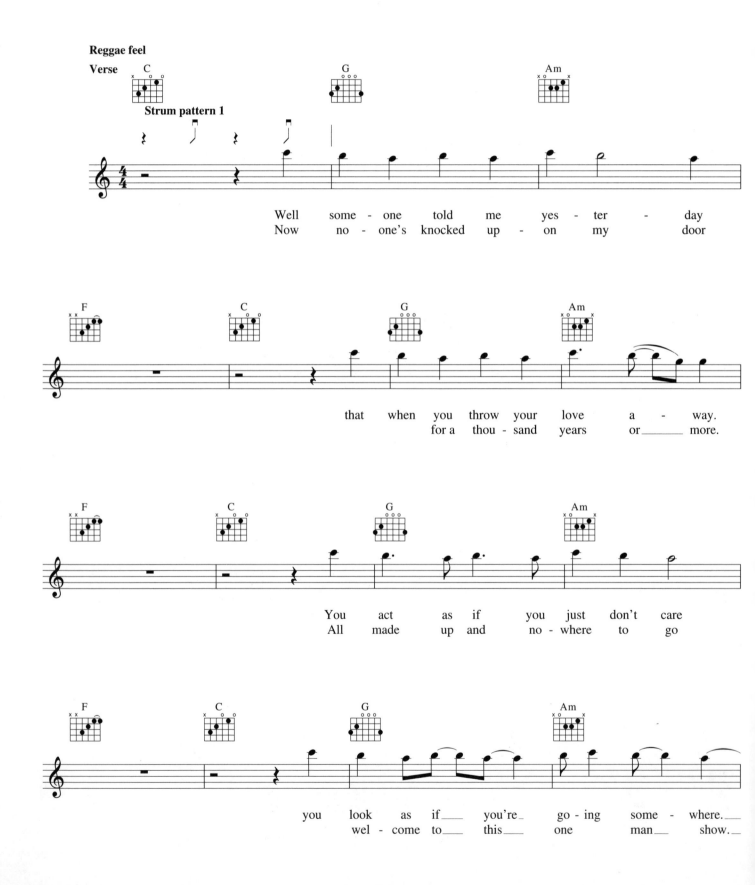

But   I   just   can't   con - vince   my - self,
Just   take   a   seat   they're   al - ways   free,

I   could - n't   live   with   no - one   else.
no   sur - prise   no   my - ste - ry.

And   I   can   on - ly
In this   thea - tre   that   I

play   that   part   and   sit   and nurse my
call   my   part   soul,   I   al - ways play the

Chorus C

Strum pattern 2

bro - ken   heart.   So   lone - ly,   so   lone - ly,
star - ring   role.

so   lone - ly,   so   lone - ly.

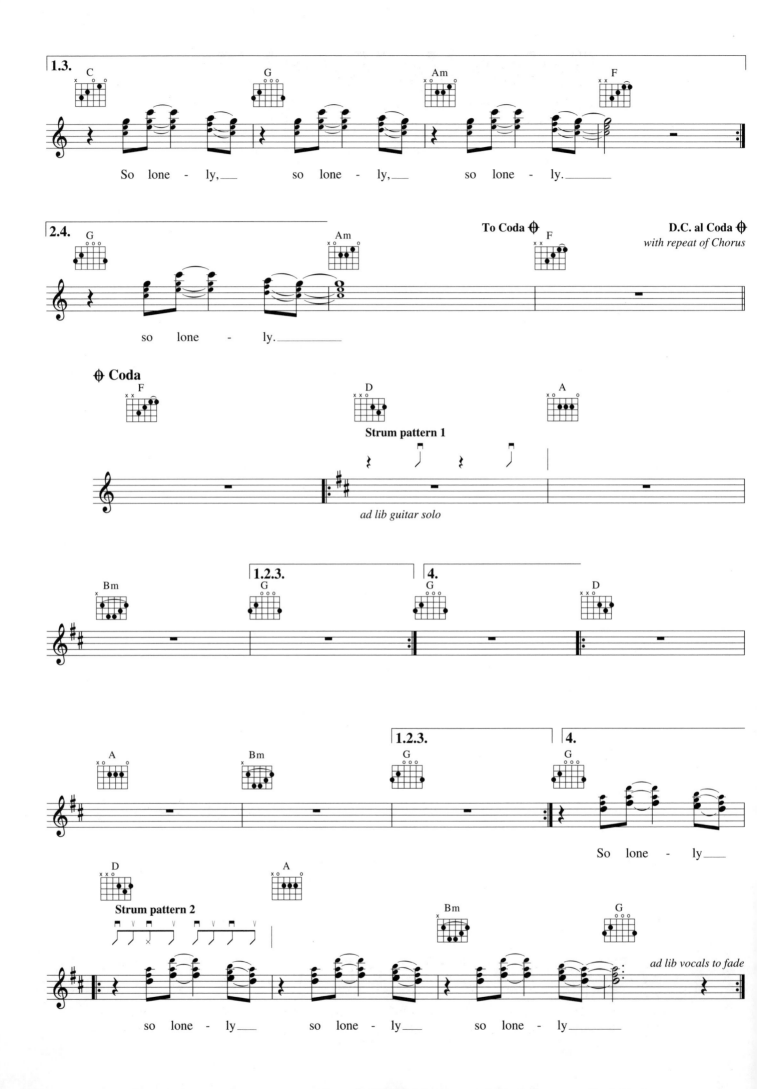

So lone - ly,___ so lone - ly,___ so lone - ly.___

so lone - ly.___

ad lib guitar solo

So lone - ly___

ad lib vocals to fade

so lone - ly___ so lone - ly___ so lone - ly___

Spice Up Your Life

Words & Music by Geri Halliwell, Emma Bunton, Melanie Brown, Melanie Chisholm, Victoria Aadams, Richard Stannard & Matt Rowe

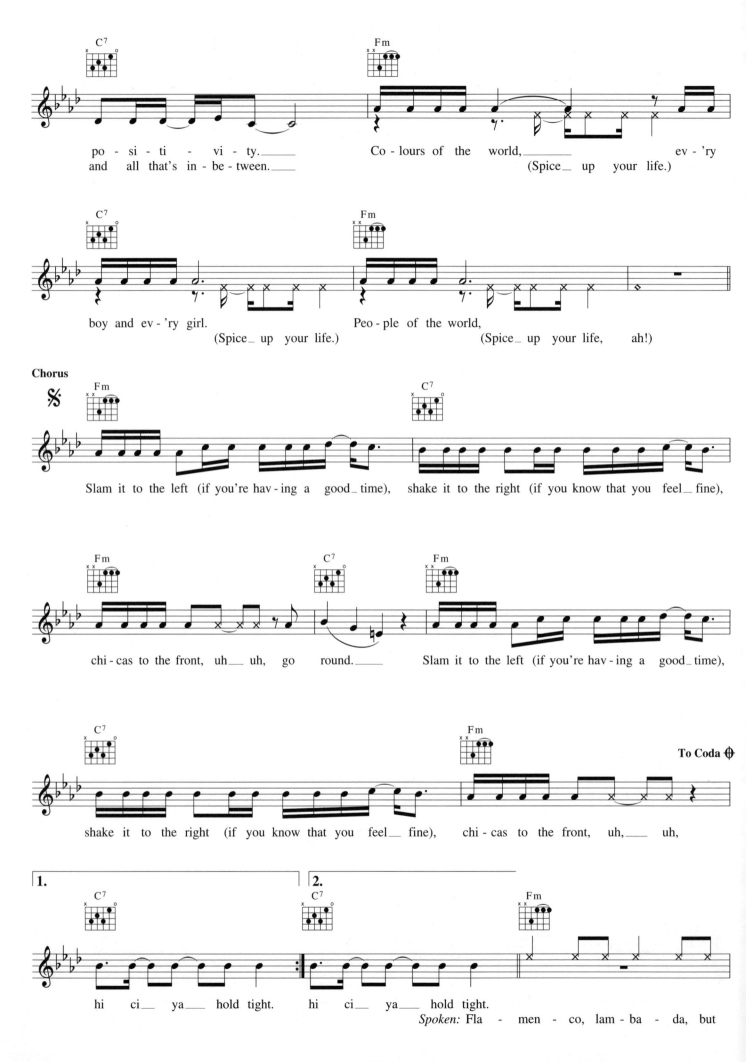

po - si - ti - vi - ty._____ Co - lours of the world,_____ ev - 'ry
and all that's in - be - tween._____ (Spice_ up your life.)

boy and ev - 'ry girl. Peo - ple of the world,
(Spice_ up your life.) (Spice_ up your life, ah!)

Chorus

Slam it to the left (if you're hav - ing a good_ time), shake it to the right (if you know that you feel_ fine),

chi - cas to the front, uh__ uh, go round._____ Slam it to the left (if you're hav - ing a good_ time),

To Coda ⊕

shake it to the right (if you know that you feel_ fine), chi - cas to the front, uh,_____ uh,

1.

hi ci_ ya___ hold tight.

2.

hi ci_ ya___ hold tight.
Spoken: Fla - men - co, lam - ba - da, but

124

hip hop is hard - er, we moon - walk the fox - trot then pol - ka the sal - sa.

D. %. al Coda ⊕

Shake it shake it shake it, ha - ka. Shake it shake it shake it, ha - ka.

⊕ Coda

hi ca__ ya__ hold tight. Slam it to the left (if you're hav - ing a good__ time),

shake it to the right (if you know that you feel__ fine), chi - cas to the front, uh,__ uh, go round._____

Slam it to the left (if you're hav - ing a good__ time), Shake it to the right (if you know that you feel__ fine),

chi - cas to the front, uh,_____ uh, hi ci__ ya_____ hold tight.

Sultans Of Swing

Words & Music by Mark Knopfler

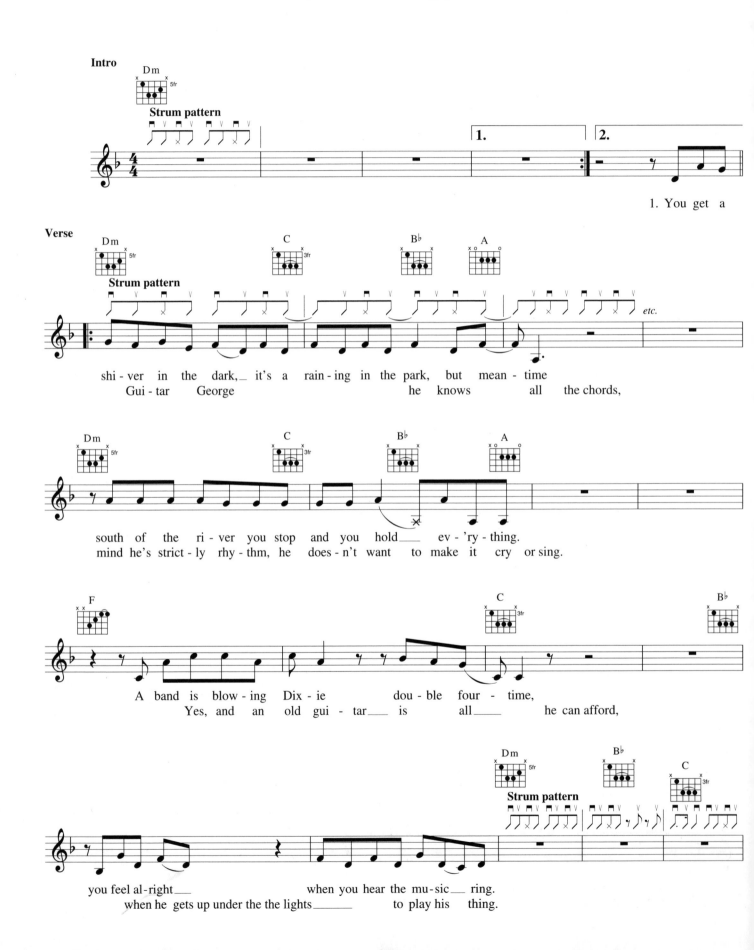

drunk and dressed in their best brown bag - gies and__ their plat - form
and says at last just as the time bell

___ soles. They don't give a damn a - bout a - ny
rings. "Good night, now it's time

trum - pet play - ing band,_____ it ain't what they call rock and roll__
to go home".___ Then he makes it fast with one more thing,_

___ And the Sul - tans,___ yeah, the
___ We are the Sultans, we are the

Sul - tans___ are play - ing cre - ole.
Sul - tans of swing.

Cre - ole

ba - by, ah, ah.

Outro solo

Strum pattern 2

Repeat to fade

128

Summertime Blues

Words & Music by Eddie Cochran & Jerry Capehart

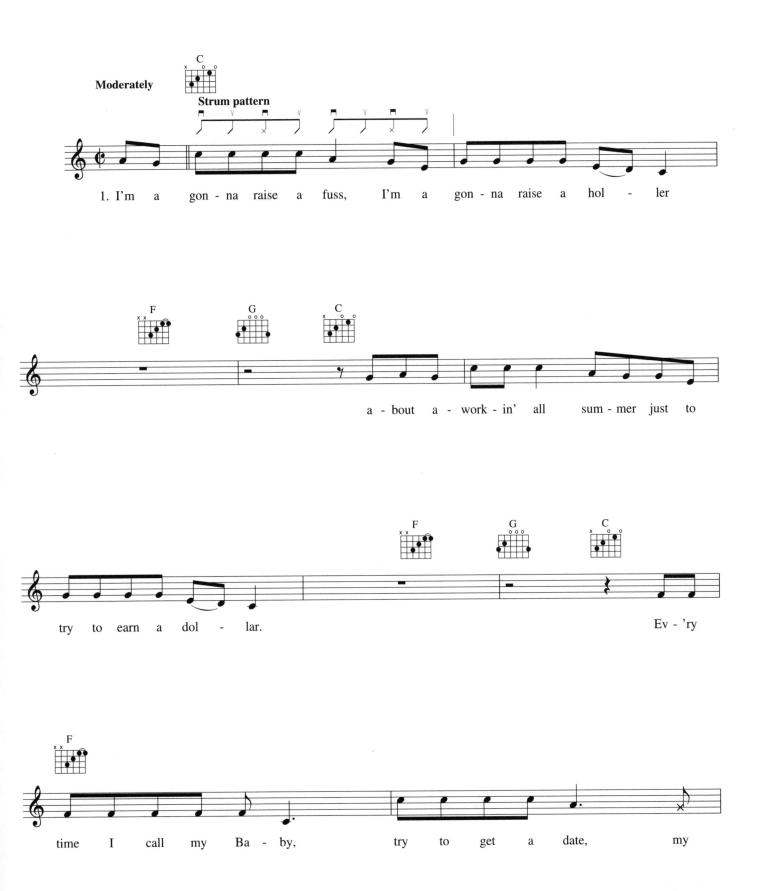

1. I'm a gon - na raise a fuss, I'm a gon - na raise a hol - ler

a - bout a - work - in' all sum - mer just to

try to earn a dol - lar. Ev - 'ry

time I call my Ba - by, try to get a date, my

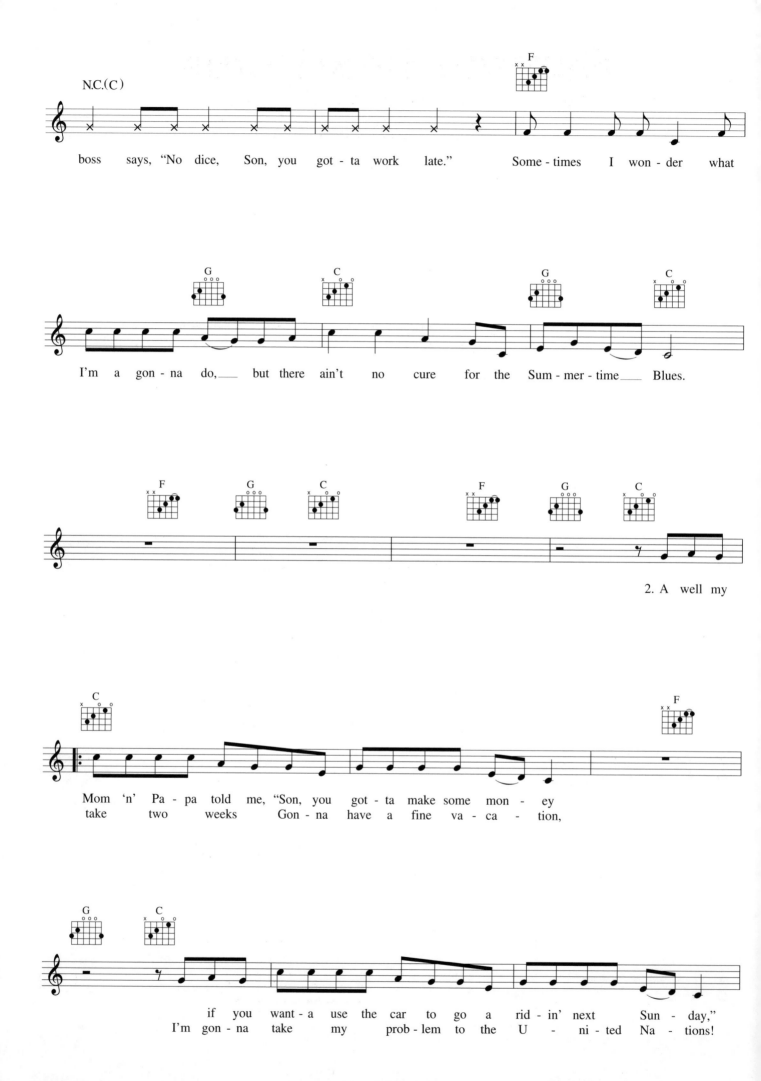

N.C.(C)

boss says, "No dice, Son, you got-ta work late." Some-times I won-der what

I'm a gon-na do,___ but there ain't no cure for the Sum-mer-time___ Blues.

2. A well my

Mom 'n' Pa-pa told me, "Son, you got-ta make some mon-ey
take two weeks Gon-na have a fine va-ca - tion,

if you want-a use the car to go a rid-in' next Sun-day,"
I'm gon-na take my prob-lem to the U - ni-ted Na-tions!

Well, I did - n't go to work told the
Well I called my Con - gress - man and

boss I was sick___ "Now you can't use the car 'cause you did - n't work a lick."
he said (quote) "I'd like to help you, Son, but you're too young to vote."

Some - times I won - der what I'm a - gon - na do,___ but there ain't no cure for the

1.

Sum - mer - time___ Blues.   3. I'm gon - na

2.

Sweet Dreams Are Made Of This

Words & Music by D. A. Stewart & A. Lennox

Sweet dreams are made of this. Who am I to dis-a-gree? I tra-vel the world and the sev-en seas. Ev-'ry-bo-dy's look-ing for some-thing. Some of them want to use you. Some of them want to get used by you. Some of them want to a-buse you. Some of them want to be

Thriller

Words & Music by Rod Temperton

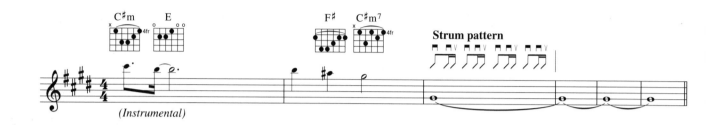

(Instrumental)

It's close to mid - night,____ and some - thin' ev - il's lurk - in' in the dark.
You hear the door____ slam____ and re - a - lize there's no - where left to run.
They're out to get____ you.____ There's de - mons clos - in' in on ev - 'ry side.

Un - der the moon - light____ you
You feel the cold____ hand,____ and
They will pos - sess____ you____ un -

see a light that al - most stops your heart.____ You try to scream,____
won - der if you'll ev - er see the sun.____ You close your eyes.____
- less you change that num - ber on your dial.____ Now is the time____

but ter - ror takes____ the sound____ be - fore____ you make____
and hope that this____ is just____ i - ma - gi - na -
for you and I____ to cud - dle close____ to - geth -

C#m7

F#7

___ it.____ You start to freeze ____ as
- tion.____ But all the while ____ you
- er. ____ And thru the night _____ I'll

C#m7   Amaj7

hor - ror looks__ you right__ be - tween ___ the eyes.___ You're pa - ra - lyzed.___
hear the crea - ture creep - ing up__ be - hind.___ You're out of time ___
save you from the ter - ror on__ the screen.___ I'll make you see ___

G#m7   C#m   E   F#   C#m7

___ 'Cause this is thril - ler ___ thril - ler night, and
___ 'Cause this is thril - ler ___ thril - ler night, there
___ that this is thril - ler ___ thril - ler night, 'cause

F#7   F#m7

no one's gon - na save ___ you from the beast ___ a - bout to strike.__ You know, it's
ain't no sec - ond chance__ a - gainst the thing ___ with for - ty eyes.__ You know it's
I could thrill you more__ than an - y ghost__ would dare to try.___ Girl this is

C#m   E   F#   C#m7

thril - ler, ___ thril - ler night. You're
thril - ler, ___ thril - ler night. You're
thril - ler, ___ thril - ler night. So

135

fight - ing for your life___ in - side a kil - ler thril - ler to -
fight - ing for you life___ in - side a
let me hold you tight___ and share a

night.___

(Instrumental)

kil - ler thril - ler to - night. Night crea - tures call and___ the

dead start___ to walk in___ their mas - que - rade. There's___

___ no___ es - cap - in'___ the jaws of___ the a - lien___ this time. They're op - en

This is___ the end of your life.___
wide

136

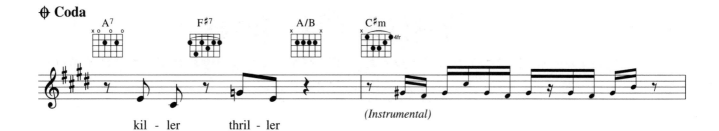

⊕ Coda

kil - ler   thril - ler

(Instrumental)

Repeat ad lib for rap

Rap:

Darkness falls across the land
The midnight hour is close at hand
Creatures crawl in search of blood
To terrorize y'awl's neighborhood
And whosoever shall be found
Without the soul for getting down
Must stand and face the hounds of hell
And rot inside a corpse's shell.

The foulest stench is in the air
The funk of forty thousand years
And grizzly ghouls from every tomb
Are closing in to seal your doom
And though you fight to stay alive
Your body starts to shiver
For no mere mortal can resist
The evil of a thriller.

Take On Me

Words by Morten Harket, Mags & Pal Waaktaar. Music by Pal Waaktaar & Mags

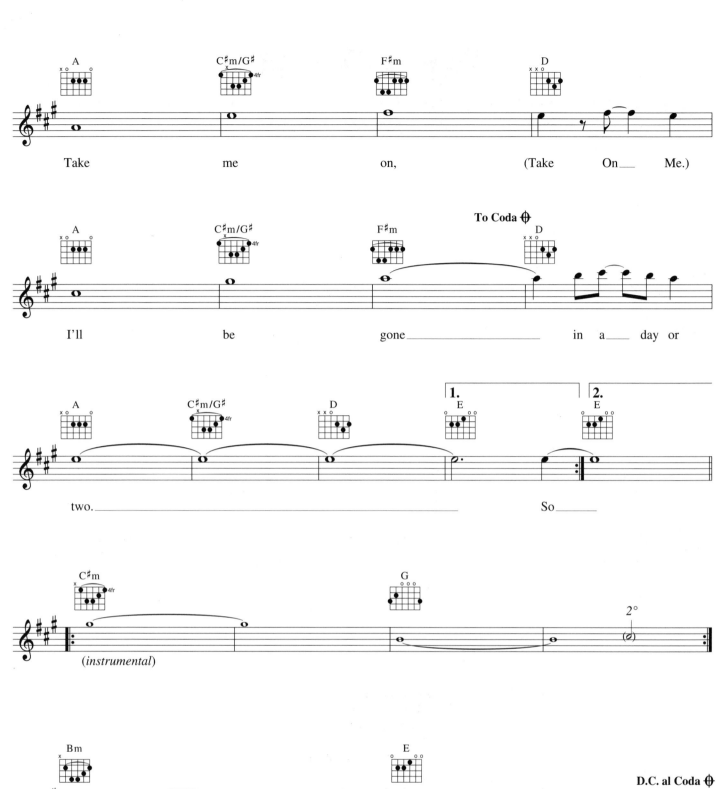

Take   me   on,   (Take   On___   Me.)

I'll   be   gone_____   in a___   day or

two._____   So____

(instrumental)

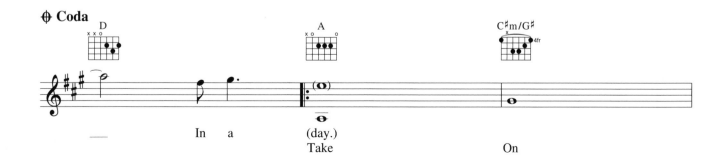

___   In   a   (day.)

Take   On

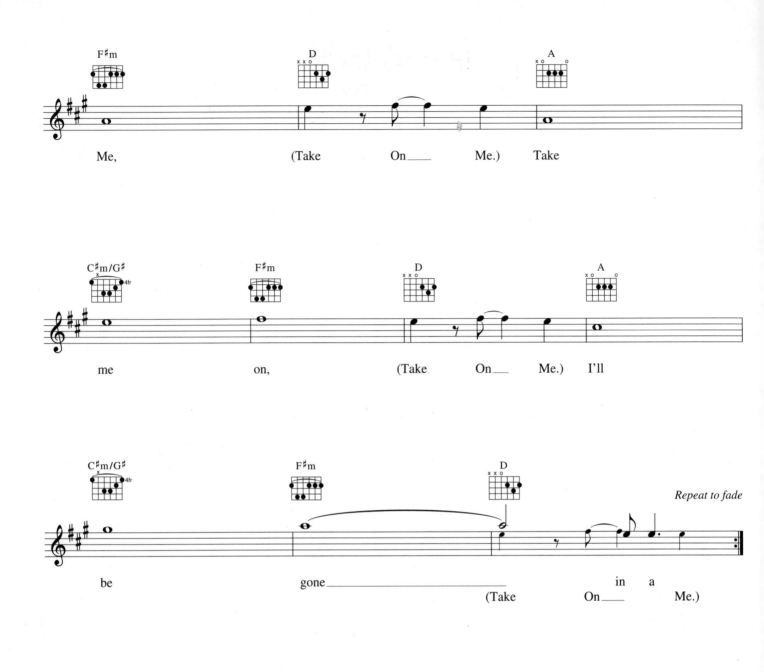

Me,   (Take   On___   Me.)   Take

me   on,   (Take   On___   Me.)   I'll

Repeat to fade

be   gone_____   in   a

(Take   On___   Me.)

Verse 2:   So, needless to say at odds and ends
                But I'll be stumbling away
                Slowly learning that life is O.K.
                Say after me
                It's much better to be safe than sorry.

Verse 3:   Oh, things that you say
                Yeah is it life or just a play
                My worries away
                You're all the things I've got to remember
                You shine away
                I'll be coming for you anyway.

Vincent

Words & Music by Don McLean

141

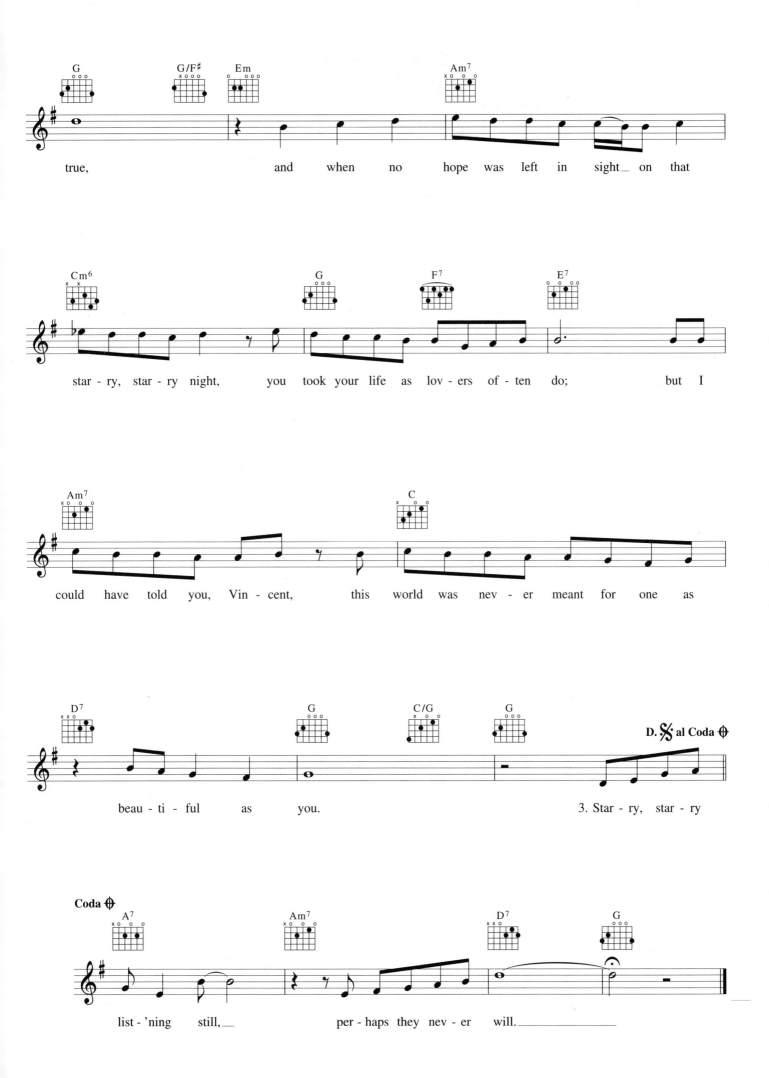

true, and when no hope was left in sight_ on that

star - ry, star - ry night, you took your life as lov - ers of - ten do; but I

could have told you, Vin - cent, this world was nev - er meant for one as

beau - ti - ful as you. 3. Star - ry, star - ry

Coda ⊕

list - 'ning still,_ per - haps they nev - er will._

143

Vienna

Words & Music by M. Ure, B. Currie, W. Cann & C. Allen

We walked in the cold____ air,____
mus - ic is weav - ing____

freez - ing breath on the win - dow pane, ly - ing and wait - ing.____
haunt - ing notes pizz - i - ca - to strings, the rhy - thm is call - ing.____

A man in the dark in the pic - ture frame so
A - lone in the night as the day - light brings a

mys - tic and soul - ful.____ A
cold emp - ty sil - ence.____ The

voice reach - ing out and a pierc - ing cry, it stays with you un - til____
warmth of your hand and a cold grey sky, it fades to the dis - tance.____

The feel-ing is gone, on-ly you and I, this means no-thing to me,
The im-age is gone, on-ly you and I, this means no-thing to me,

this means no-thing to me._____ Oh,_____ Vi -
this means no-thing to me._____

To Coda

- en - na._____ (Intrumental)

1. 2.

2. The This means

Coda

145

Walk Of Life

Words & Music by Mark Knopfler

Here comes John - ny sing - ing old - ies gold - ies, be bop - a - lu - la ba - by

(Verse 2 see block lyric)

what I say.___ Here comes John - ny sing - ing I Got - ta Wo - man,

down in the tun - nels trying to make it pay. He got the act - ion,

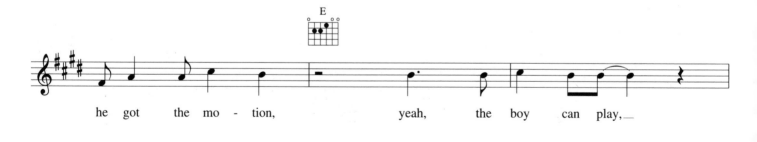

he got the mo - tion, yeah, the boy can play,___

de - di - ca - tion,___ de - vo - tion, turn - ing all the night time

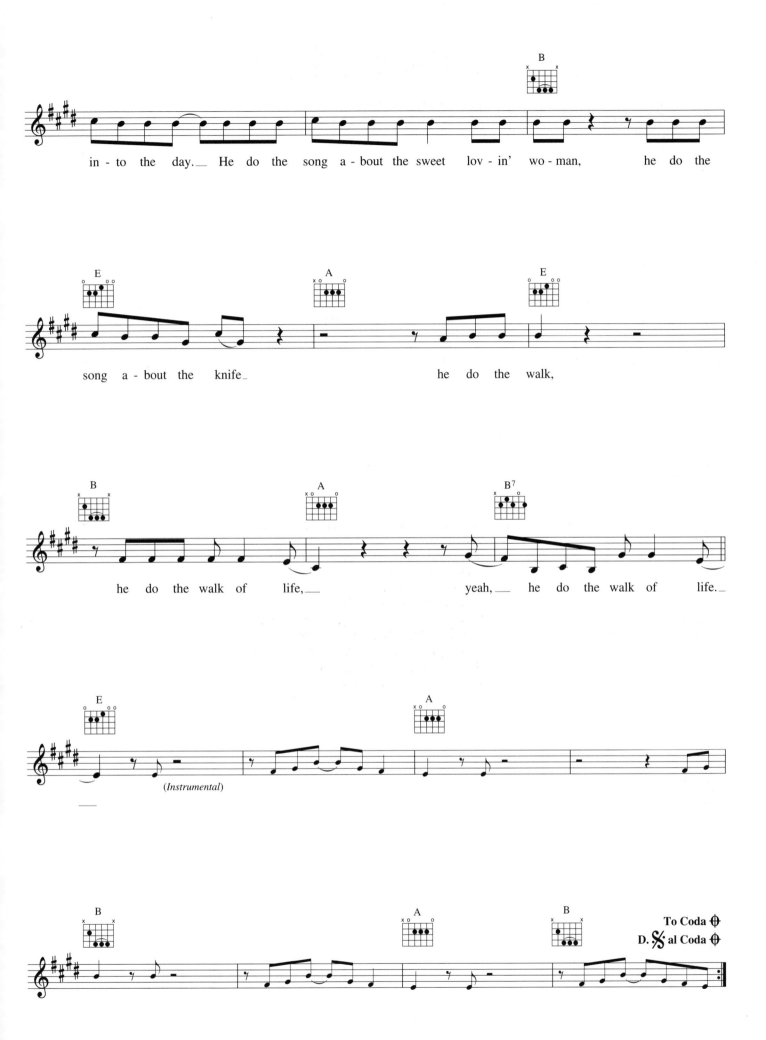

in - to the day.__ He do the song a - bout the sweet lov - in' wo - man, he do the

song a - bout the knife __ he do the walk,

he do the walk of life, __ yeah, __ he do the walk of life. __

(Instrumental)

To Coda ⊕
D. %. al Coda ⊕

⊕ Coda

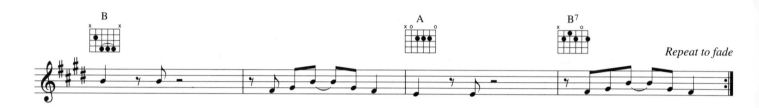

Repeat to fade

Verse 2:   Here comes Johnny and he'll tell you a story
Hand me down my walkin' shoes
Here comes Johnny with the power and glory
Backbeat the talkin' blues.
He got the action, he got the motion
Yeah, the boy can play dictation
Devotion turning all the night time into day.
And after all the violence and double talk
There's just a song in all the trouble and strife
He do the walk, you do the walk of life
Mmm, you do the walk of life.

148

What's Love Got To Do With It

Words & Music by Graham Lyle & Terry Britten

Chorus

____ what's love____ got to do, got to do with it? What's love____ but a

sec - ond hand e - mo - tion? What's love____ got to do, got to do with it?

1. Who needs a heart when a heart can be bro - ken? It **2.** heart can be bro - ken?

(Instrumental)

I've been tak - ing on a

Verse 2:   It may seem to you
            That I'm acting confused
            When you're close to me
            If I tend to look dazed
            I read it in some place
            I've got cause to be
            There's a name for it
            There's a phrase that fits
            But whatever the reason
            You do it for me.

Wild Wood

Words & Music by Paul Weller

Verse 2:   Don't let them get you down
Making you feel guilty about
Golden rain will bring you riches
All the good things you deserve now.

Verse 3:   Climbing, forever trying
Find your way out of the wild wild wood
Now there's no justice
You've only yourself that you can trust in.

Verse 4:   And I said high tide, mid-afternoon
People fly by in the traffic's boom
Knowing just where you're blowing
Getting to where you should be going.

Verse 5:   Day by day your world fades away
Waiting to feel all the dreams that say
Golden rain will bring you riches
All the good things you deserve now.

Without You

Words & Music by Peter Ham & Tom Evans

No I can't for-get this ev-'ning or your

face as you were leav-ing, but I guess that's just the way the sto-ry goes. You al-ways

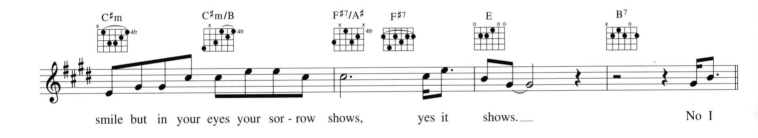

smile but in your eyes your sor-row shows, yes it shows. No I

can't for-get to-mor-row when I think of all my sor-row and I had you there but then I let you

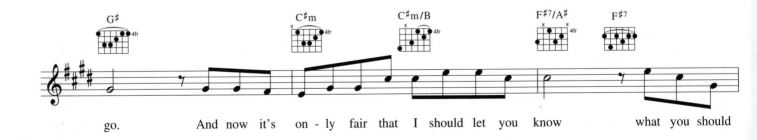

go. And now it's on-ly fair that I should let you know what you should

You Do Something To Me

Words & Music by Paul Weller

You Give Love A Bad Name

Words & Music by Jon Bon Jovi, Richie Sambora & Desmond Child

Shot thru' the heart, And you're to blame. Dar-lin', You give love a bad name.

An An-gel's smile is what you sell, you
paint your smile on your lips,

pro - mise me hea - ven, then put me thru' hell. Chains of____ love,____ got a
blood - red nails on your fin - ger tips. School - boy's____ dream,_ you

hold on me. When pas - sion's a pri - son, you can't break_ free.
act so shy. You ve - ry first kiss was your first kiss good - bye.

F

Oh,_____ You're a load - ed gun._

Bb   **F**

Oh,_____ There's No - where to run. No - one can save me, the

G

Chorus

Cm   Ab   Bb   Cm

Strum pattern

da - mage is done.   Shot through the heart,_   And you're to_ blame.

Ab   Bb   Eb   Cm   Ab

You give love____ a bad name, Bad name. I play my part_ and you

Bb   Cm   Ab   Bb   Eb   Cm

play your_ game,   you give love____ a bad name, Bad name. Oh,

159

you give love,_____ a bad name.

Strum pattern

2. You ___

Shot through the heart___ and you're to ___ blame, you give love_____ a

bad name, (Bad name.) I play my part,___ and you play your_ game.

you give love_____ a bad name, (Bad name.) You give love,_____

Repeat and fade

you give love,_____ a bad name.

3/02(43011)